THE
SOCIAL PROBLEM
OF MENTAL DEFICIENCY

THE
SOCIAL PROBLEM
OF MENTAL DEFICIENCY

by N. O'CONNOR, M.A., Ph.D.

and

J. TIZARD, M.A., B.Litt., Ph.D.

Medical Research Council, Social Psychiatry Research Unit
Maudsley Hospital, London

with a foreword by
Professor AUBREY LEWIS, M.D., F.R.C.P.

PERGAMON PRESS

LONDON & NEW YORK

1956

Published by Pergamon Press
4 & 5 Fitzroy Square, London W.1
and 122 E. 55th Street, New York 22, N.Y.
Printed in Great Britain by
Robert MacLehose and Co. Ltd, Glasgow, Scotland

CONTENTS

FOREWORD

MENTAL deficiency is a rewarding field for systematic inquiry. It has the advantages that its salient phenomena are less diverse and elusive, and lend themselves rather more readily to measurement, than those of most other branches of psychiatry. Our knowledge of it has been furthered by methods drawn, on the one hand, from clinical medicine and pathology and, on the other, from the social sciences and genetics. The work of psychologists, in particular, has been indispensable: it has been most striking in the cognitive studies through which BINET and others made their outstanding contributions to the subject.

Among contemporary psychologists Dr. O'CONNOR and Dr. TIZARD have been conspicuously active in this territory for the last six years. Their series of experiments has made clearer the stages and measures necessary in carrying through a process of orderly training, designed to lead the defective back to contented and useful life in the general community. They have at the same time scrutinized the social and administrative arrangements for recognizing defectives and caring for them: they could hardly refrain from doing so since these are part of the social situation which determines how much can be achieved by any study aimed at bettering the lot of the mentally defective. This aim has been explicit in the investigations described in the following pages, though issues of a more theoretical or general nature have also been examined, and problems of motivation, for example, explored.

Doctors sometimes—borrowing a term from another profession —call the rest of mankind laymen. The labours of such laymen have been essential to the progress of medicine. In mental deficiency, most clearly, the joint efforts of laymen and physicians have been essential for advancing the subject; the work done in the Social Psychiatry Research Unit and described in this book illustrates how fruitful can be the collaboration of psychologist and psychiatrist to this end.

AUBREY LEWIS

AUTHORS' PREFACE

OUR MAIN purpose in writing this book has been to summarize work on mental deficiency carried out by members of the Medical Research Council's Social Psychiatry Research Unit. This Unit was established in 1948, under the Honorary Direction of Professor AUBREY LEWIS, to investigate occupational and social aspects of psychiatry. The experimental studies described in Chapters 5–9 owe much to his wise counsel. Many of the studies were carried out by or with our colleagues Drs. K. A. YONGE, F. M. LOOS, S. GORDON, M. WEINER, J. H. CHAMPNESS and G. S. CLARIDGE. We have endeavoured to place the work in its historical and social setting, and have included some reference to the work of other investigators; but we have not attempted to review the literature as a whole, or to describe in detail the excellent work being done by others in the field of mental deficiency.

In Chapter 10 we have expressed opinions about the law and the mental deficiency services in England. It will be appreciated that here we give our personal views only.

Throughout our investigations we have enjoyed the hospitality of Dr. J. K. COLLIER LAING and the Darenth and Stone Hospital Management Committee, and Dr. J. F. MACMAHON and the Manor Hospital Committee. Dr. A. D. B. CLARKE, and Dr. A. M. CLARKE, psychologists at the Manor Hospital, have been generous and disinterested colleagues with whom we have worked in close association. Dr. J. M. CRAWFORD, now Physician Superintendent of Botleys Park, and Dr. G. M. TUCKER of Darenth Park, gave us a great deal of help in the early stages of the research. To all of these, and to our colleagues in the Unit and the Institute of Psychiatry we wish to express our indebtedness.

The title of the book indicates the field of study. We have, however, looked at "the social problem of mental deficiency" from a psychological viewpoint. It will be obvious to the reader that the geneticist, sociologist or social caseworker would have seen a somewhat different picture.

For permission to include material which has already appeared in article form we are indebted to the following editors and pub-

lishers: *Bull. Wld. Hlth. Org.* for material in Chapter 2; Professor
L. S. PENROSE and Sidgwick & Jackson for the quotation on p. 18,
from *The Biology of Mental Defect* (1949), *Brit. med. J.* for data on
London Survey and Tables 7–13; *J. ment. Sci.* for Table 16;
Professor R. L. THORNDIKE and John Wiley & Sons for Table 18
from *Personnel Selection; Test and Measurement Techniques* (1949);
the *Lancet* for some of the material in Chapters 6 and 7, and for
Tables 27 and 28; *Amer. J. ment. Def.* for material in Chapter 7;
Brit. J. Psychol. for Figs. 1 and 2, and *Amer. J. ment. Def.* for Fig.
3; *J. genet. Psychol.* for Tables 32 and 33; Dr. L. G. LOWREY and
The Ronald Press Co. for material on pp. 149–150 from the article
"Delinquent and criminal personalities" in *Personality and the
Behaviour Disorders* (J. McV. HUNT, ed.), II (1944); Professor J.
E. W. WALLIN and Staples Press for Table 34 from *Children with
Mental and Physical Handicaps* (1949); Dr. CROSS and *Brit. J. prev.
soc. Med.* for Table 15 and Table on p. 156.

CHAPTER ONE

HISTORICAL BACKGROUND

DURING the last 80 years the passing of two important Acts and the publication of two official reports have reflected the growing public interest in the care of mental defectives. The Acts were the Idiots Act of 1886 and the 1913 Mental Deficiency Act. The reports were those of the Royal Commission on the Care and Control of the Feeble-minded, of 1908, and the Interdepartmental Committee (Wood Report) of 1929. Other important legislation has been that concerning special educational provision for the backward. Following the 1870 Education Act and the report of a Departmental Committee on Educable and Non-educable Children set up in 1897, the Elementary Education (Defective and Epileptic Children) Act of 1899 and the 1944 Education Act both expressed new attitudes to the problem of backwardness.

The extensive developments mentioned above are part of a relatively modern phase of the history of care. So far as western Europe is concerned, mental deficiency began to receive systematic attention before 1789. Even earlier attention to the condition now called mental deficiency was given in England in the reign of Edward I. At that time a distinction was made between idiots and lunatics. This distinction was given legal sanction because of the laws of inheritance of property. Any person who had lost his reason was presumed to be capable of regaining it and hence of regaining also his capacity to manage estates, whereas "born fools" were deemed never to have had understanding and might therefore be deprived of their rights of inheritance. The term "idiot" is itself much older, being a word of Greek origin connoting a "private" person in the sense of one who is cut off from communication with his fellows.

Theories of the Education of Defectives

The systematic study of the condition of mental defect arose from the attempt to educate the deaf. J. RODRIGUEZ PEREIRE, a Spanish teacher of the deaf, is the acknowledged originator of the

1

2 *The Social Problem of Mental Deficiency*

movement to educate the backward or "idiot", a movement which however probably owes most to his successors in France and Switzerland, notably ITARD, SEGUIN and to a lesser extent, GUGGENBUEHL. Before 1780 PEREIRE was training the senses of deaf pupils.

The application of his techniques to the education of mental defectives represents in this period the triumph of a belief in Sensationism, and the dominance of a Lockeian empiricist view of epistemology. It assumed in other words that to train the senses was to train the mind and that deficiencies in the latter could be corrected by making up presumed deficiences in sense knowledge and sense power. Even at this time when ITARD and SEGUIN supported such a view, Pinel opposed to it a contrary opinion, then called Nativism, namely that knowledge, or the capacity to acquire it, is not educable but inherited.

A great deal could be said about the very interesting techniques developed by the Sensationists and about the more modern educational techniques to which their work gave rise, such as those of DESCOEUDRES and Madame MONTESSORI. At the turn of the eighteenth century the key experiment was that carried out by ITARD with an idiot boy found in the woods of Aveyron in 1799. This experiment revealed both the strengths and weaknesses of the Sensationist theory.

The idiot boy called Victor was found living like an animal, with no social interests or skills. ITARD attempted to train him to lead a normal life, herein acting against the advice of PINEL. ITARD'S successes were notable but limited. The boy learned a number of skills, even the elementary use of letters and simple words, but remained attached to an outdoor life. He was unable to generalize on the basis of the special training which he had been given. ITARD described Victor as lacking even in the ability to distinguish heat and cold, and set about his education on the basis of this simple fact. He claimed that hot baths could help to train the sense of touch. When the idiot boy gained an appreciation of warmth, he was then able to see the value of clothing and from that point could be induced to learn to dress himself.

Proceeding in this manner ITARD aimed to train all the senses and so provide the young man with a more favourable opportunity to enjoy social contact. His efforts were successful to the extent that he was finally able to teach Victor the use of simple combinations of letters, and most of the arts of self care. His final state was very different from that of the normal adolescent, but the changes achieved by education were a remarkable testimony to the value of the training and treatment of grossly backward people.

This experiment has not been repeated, but in his clinical work SEGUIN continued ITARD'S principles of education through the senses and succeeded in training hospital inmates in the skills of eating, dressing and personal care. His book on *The Psychological Treatment, Hygiene and Education of Idiots* (1846), is a fascinating storehouse of suggestions concerning the training of defectives which in certain respects anticipate later work by half a century. What is of interest today is his advances along the lines laid down by PINEL concerning work treatment. Despite his Nativist views PINEL, in his *Treatise on Alienism* (1806), states that the fundamental principle of the hospital treatment of defectives and the insane is a constant round of mechanical work which both trains the faculties and prevents the recurrence of disturbing thoughts. SEGUIN accepted this principle and through his work in America, where he went in 1848, did much to lay the foundations of hospital treatment there.

The educational movement popular at this time was later strongly criticized. BINET, at the end of the nineteenth century, reinforcing the Nativist opposition to Sensationism, carried out investigations which had a profound effect on informed theory concerning the care of defectives. The influence of this movement is still very strong in current English mental-deficiency practice, and its reverberations in educational theory lie at the basis of much current controversy concerning educational selection.

From 1890 onwards, and as a result of the growing importance of universal primary education, the problem of those who could not learn was first given serious attention by psychologists and educationists. Findings in studies made in Berlin, Paris, Brussels and London during the next thirty years gradually led to the view that a great deal of effort was being expended by teachers in schools and in some cases by educational trainers in hospitals, in attempting to educate the ineducable. BINET'S views, expressed in his book with Simon, *Mentally Defective Children* (1914), were that the Sensationists had made a serious error in neglecting to apply rigorous methodology to their investigations, and had in their enthusiasm failed to evaluate the results of their efforts. Some of his own studies showed that the attempt to educate the mentally deficient often led to no improvement. As BINET is often quoted as an authority, it is also worth noting that this point of view, taken up in critizing his predecessors, was only one of his opinions. Another, which appears equally frequently in his writings, is that no matter how difficult it may be to teach the backward, every effort must be made to equip them with the minimum essential social skills of reading and writing. But such was the force of the swing away from Sensationism that this point of view is now seldom quoted and BINET is remembered for his intelligence tests and his attacks on the unwarranted optimism of ITARD and SEGUIN.

The studies of the genetics of mental deficiency during the early years of this century were thought to offer strong support for the view that a great deal of mental defect was inherited. Such studies were made by GODDARD in America of large families arising from the union of presumed defectives. They appeared to show that the high birth rate common in a section of the population which was described as the "submerged tenth" threatened to overwhelm the better endowed sections of the community in future generations. The fear of what was called "National Degeneracy" led A. F. TREDGOLD to advocate segregation of defectives as a measure to limit their too rapid procreation. This view he, one of the leading experts in the field, continued to support in all editions of his standard text on mental deficiency from the first edition in 1908 to the most recent edition by A. F. and R. F. TREDGOLD in 1951. In America, both sterilization and segregation of defectives were introduced as remedies. In some American states sterilization continues to be carried out.

Discussions centring around views on inheritance were common in the period before the passing of the 1913 Mental Deficiency Act and may have influenced some of the mental deficiency practice which followed. For example, a Statutory Instrument was added to this Act after it became law, one of the 41 parts of which aims to prevent any attachment of a defective on licence with a member of the opposite sex. This rule is still in force.*

Much of the evidence of these early genetic studies is now considered to be less convincing than it was at the time, but echoes of the original discussion still influence the controversy concerning the intelligence quotients of children of different socio-economic levels. One point at issue in this discussion is whether the lower intelligence level of children from poor homes compared with that of the children of the well-to-do is due to overcrowding and hard conditions of life as BINET thought, or to poorer genetic stock. Another aspect of the problem is whether a differential birth rate gives rise to a declining level of national intelligence. The most recent evidence, that of the Scottish Council for Research in Education (1949), suggests that this is not proven.

It is certainly the case that the movement begun by BINET on the one hand in the field of education, and by such workers as GODDARD in genetics, had the effect of transferring attention from educational techniques to eugenic practices such as segregation. The eugenic theory received strong support during the 1930's because of the crippling economic recession. This made it impossible for many of the mentally backward to get work, or for their parents to support them. Thus those who advocated segregation as a eugenic measure could also point to the employment difficulties to which more backward members of the community were subject. At this period therefore the certification and hospitalization of large numbers of defectives appeared to be justified both eugenically and economically.

If the period 1789–1890 is regarded as a first period of optimism in the treatment of the backward and the period 1890–1939 as a second period of relative pessimism, the years since the last war are chiefly characterized by a new swing to a point of view of modified optimism. Undoubtedly the era of relatively stable economic prosperity and full employment has been largely responsible for this change, in so far as it has made possible a demand for labour to such a degree that even seriously handicapped persons can find employment. But in addition there has been a relaxation of anxiety

---

* There was of course an additional reason for this regulation, namely, the assumption that defectives are likely to make inefficient parents.

concerning the position of the defective in society; the theory of physical and mental degeneracy or declining national intelligence can no longer be supported with overwhelming confidence. At the same time a number of experiments which will be referred to in subsequent chapters have shown two things. The first is that many institutional defectives can do simple tasks in industry, either as machine minders or unskilled labourers, and the second is that they do not seem to be such a danger to the community as was formerly supposed. Whilst there are undoubtedly defectives who are also criminals, it is now known that they are not large in number and it is uncertain whether their criminality is more a product of their defect than of some social cause. There no longer appears to be such a need for the mentally deficient to be segregated from the community, and many who would hitherto have been certified and cared for in hospital may now be thought fit to work and live as free citizens. In some cases they may need extra help and guidance, but perhaps no more than should be accorded to many physically disabled persons.

No one now regards idiots and imbeciles, the two most handicapped groups of mental defectives, as fully educable, although perhaps ITARD and SEGUIN would have thought so. There is good pathological evidence that their brains are extensively damaged in most cases. None the less, despite the fact that idiots are known to have extensive brain damage, their educability is not a simple function of their pathology, and there is a good case for attempting to fit higher-grade defectives for life in the community.

Recent Provision for Care and Training

Whilst there is now a long history of theory and of training techniques dating back nearly two centuries, the first hospitals in England for the care of "idiots" were established about 100 years ago. One of the first, The Royal Earlswood Asylum, was established in 1847. As the Royal Commission on the Care and Control of the Feeble-Minded pointed out in 1908, the building of hospitals for the care of idiots began before the passing of the Idiots Act of 1886, by which time there were four large hospitals in being. These grew up because of a charitable movement for the care of idiots and imbeciles. Another quite separate movement led to the building of other institutions for the care of the feeble-minded. This second movement arose out of the work of two societies, the National Association for Promoting the Welfare of the Feeble-Minded, founded in 1895, and the Lancashire and Cheshire Society for the Permanent Care of the Feeble-Minded, founded in 1902. It was only between the years 1847 and 1895 that the words imbecile and feeble-minded began to come into common use to distinguish different grades of mental defect hitherto comprehended under the term "idiot". During this period and until 1908 confusion in the use of these terms was common just as the original distinction between idiots and lunatics was somewhat confused by the use, in the Lunacy Act of 1890, of the term "idiot" in its definition of lunacy. The purpose of hospitals before this time was to care for defectives of all grades, whether for private payment or on the basis of payment by the local authority. It seems likely that most of the cases cared for in such a hospital as the Royal Earlswood were imbeciles and idiots, but a few would have been feeble-minded. Some hospitals, such as Darenth Park, originally founded as schools for imbeciles, later became training colonies for the feeble-minded.

Subsequently, as a result of the recommendations of the 1908 Commission and the 1913 Mental Deficiency Act, the three terms, Idiot, Imbecile and Feeble-Minded have come to have relatively distinct denotations. Practising psychologists generally accept different Intelligence Quotients as characteristic of the three conditions although in law they continue to be defined in terms of the social ability and competence of the person concerned and the I.Q. forms at best only a rough dividing line.

Many of the institutions in being at this time, that is in 1890 or 1910 had an educational aim, but as BINET had shown in France at the Bicêtre and other hospitals, this training was mainly ineffective in turning out socially competent citizens. Fewer than 15 per cent of patients discharged from the Royal Earlswood Asylum between 1893 and 1908 were socially useful in any sense and only $3\frac{1}{4}$ per cent were earning wages. In view of the considerably greater success which will be reported below, such low figures must be accounted for in terms of a high proportion of idiots and imbeciles on the one hand and the poor demand for labour on the other. For example at another institution, Starcross, the Royal Commission found that a higher proportion could earn wages because a much higher proportion were of feeble-minded or high-grade imbecile level. Even so the number of successes was not great despite the fact that training and education was mainly manual or industrial.

Some conception of the limited provision for defectives at the time when the first Mental Deficiency Act was passed can be gleaned from the following quotation.

"When the Act came into force, there were in hospitals, institutions and licensed houses registered under the Idiots Act, 1886, 2,163 patients. At the end of the year additional accommodation had been provided in certified institutions, certified houses, and approved homes for a total of 2,959 cases. At the same time there were 16 cases under Guardianship, and 84 other cases in single care, but not notified under the Mental Deficiency Act, had been notified to us." (*Board of Control Annual Report*, 1914.)

Additional institutions for the care of the feeble-minded at this time numbered about eight, most of them catering for approximately twenty patients. Many other homes existed to take care of young men and women who were not regarded as feeble-minded. For example, about 10 per cent of the girls dealt with by one organization for helping servants were thought to be of lower than normal intelligence, but evidence is scanty. Reformatories, Poor Law Institutions and prisons frequently housed feeble-minded men and women.

Thus before the 1913 Mental Deficiency Act the provision for the care of the feeble-minded was virtually non-existent when compared with the numbers now resident in mental deficiency colonies or subject to other forms of care such as Guardianship and Statutory Supervision. Statistics since that date based on Board of Control Reports will make this clear.

It will be seen that Guardianship has increased more than twentyfold since 1916 compared with an increase in hospital provision of about nine times the 1916 figures. (Guardianship refers to a form of care in which a patient is regarded as subject to an order for care but in which he may be placed in a private family and the cost of his keep provided by the Local Health Authority. The term

Table 1. *Number of Patients under Care*

	Patients in Institutions	On Licence from Institutions	Guardian-ship	Notified (section 51 cases)	Statutory Super-vision
1916	6,612	—	136	88	—
1920	11,675	—	279	72	—
1925	20,297	—	635	150	—
1930	28,234	1,327	1,873	247	24,710
1935	40,256	2,437	3,381	264	34,840
1940	48,392	3,642	4,813	319	38,847
1945	52,788	5,286	4,678	338	41,804
1951	57,661	5,266	3,394	456	50,049

Statutory Supervision on the other hand refers to a form of community care in which an individual may remain in his own home, where he is visited by a representative of the Local Health Authority for the purpose of insuring that his care continues to be satisfactory. He is thus not subject to a Magistrate's Order.

The increase in hospital provision between 1915 and 1950 marks an attempt to deal with the social and genetic problem which gave rise to the Commissions and the Acts mentioned above. During the period since 1913 however, a gradual alteration of emphasis may be noted in the tendency to make more provision for the extra-mural care of the mentally defective. Thus for example, after 1928, shortly following the second Mental Deficiency Act of 1927, the Board of Control Reports, that is the reports of the body set up in 1913 to supervise the operation of the Act, show an increasing number of patients dealt with in occupation centres. At that time most of these centres were run by voluntary organizations, and as late as 1938 the number of such centres still exceeded those managed by local authorities. These centres were intended to supply training for children who had been found ineducable, or for adults who had been deemed ineducable during school years. Table 2 provides a list of the number of centres and the number of patients catered for from 1928 to 1954.

Since the war the numbers have increased to over 12,000. Details of occupation centres are given in Chapter 3.

This trend towards increasing the number of defectives under extra-mural care, and the post-war investigations to be reported

B

Table 2. Patients in Occupation Centres

							Mentally defective
	1928	104	Centres catered for			1,452	persons
in	1930	171	,,	,,	,,	2,708	,,
in	1935	192	,,	,,	,,	4,008	,,
in	1938	191	,,	,,	,,	4,244	,,
in	1950	195	,,	,,	,,	6,318	,,
in	1954	255	,,	,,	,,	10,942	,,

below, reinforce the view that most of the feeble-minded can live
satisfactorily outside hospitals, as indeed many already do. It is
possible that this point of view was forcing itself upon the notice
of the Administrators as early as 1928. The Board of Control
Reports, especially that of 1928, and until 1939, frequently refer to
the possibilities of the extra-mural employment of defectives. The
Royal Commission of 1908, however, received a great deal of
evidence tending to show that the possibilities for the employment
of defectives at that time were extremely limited.

The Plan of this Book

This chapter has introduced the subject of mental deficiency and
the problems of care. It has attempted to show that two different
attitudes to the theory of the cause and treatment of mental
defectives have in the past led to two kinds of administrative
practice. In subsequent chapters arguments will be advanced in
support of the view that in a high proportion of cases defectives
can be largely self-supporting and may cease to be cases for
hospitalization. In many instances, it is suggested, they may cease
to be subject to a Mental Deficiency Law and be dealt with under
the Education Acts, the National Health Service Act or other
appropriate existing Legislation.

This book is divided into chapters as follows: Chapter 2 deals
with the prevalence of mental deficiency. In Chapter 3 the mental-
deficiency services are described. Chapters 4 and 5 report the
results of some psychometric investigations and relate these
studies to occupational success. In Chapters 6 and 7 techniques
of training defectives are examined. These techniques are related
to occupational success in Chapter 8. A special problem of the
treatment of unstable defectives is discussed in Chapter 9. In

Chapter 10 certain proposals for a future service for defectives are put forward, firstly in relation to the law and secondly in relation to administrative provision. Finally, in Chapter 11, the work is summarized and certain inferences drawn concerning past practice and plans for the future.

CHAPTER TWO

THE PREVALENCE OF MENTAL DEFICIENCY

Criteria of Mental Deficiency

IN DECIDING whether a person is or is not mentally defective six aspects of his present condition are considered relevant: (*a*) anatomical and physiological: (*b*) intellectual: (*c*) educational: (*d*) social (social competence): (*e*) occupational: and (*f*) temperamental or moral. Historical and family circumstances are also considered. Among these are the socio-economic status and occupational competence of other members of the family, the family history and the individual's own developmental and educational history. For a diagnosis of mental deficiency to be made the defect must have been manifest at birth or during childhood or adolescence (for a distinction is made in psychiatry between mental deficiency and mental deterioration or dementia occurring in later life). Many writers insist too that the condition must be an "incurable" one, though for diagnostic purposes this qualification, which for other reasons is misleading, appears to be superfluous.

Diagnosis of severe and moderate subnormality—idiocy and imbecility—is comparatively easy to make, at least by the time a child has reached school age, since functional deficit is both general and marked. Physiological and developmental criteria are employed, and these are supplemented by intelligence testing or other diagnostic assessment. To diagnose mental deficiency of mild grade, however (feeble-mindedness), criteria are employed which depend to a considerable extent on social and educational factors. Difficulties then arise for a number of reasons.

1. The criteria themselves are unreliably measured. An individual's performance even on intelligence tests, which are more reliable than most of the other measures used to diagnose mental subnormality, is by no means constant from one test to another. And though, when a group of children is tested and retested on a standard measure such as the Binet test, the average intelligence quotient (I.Q.) remains much the same, the I.Q.s of individuals

vary considerably. One reason for this individual variation is the unreliability of the measurements. And where assessments of sub-normality depend on clinical judgments of social or occupational success the extent of error is certainly greater.

2. A further difficulty of interpretation, in the case of most intelligence tests and other measures which have no absolute scale of measurement but are scored in terms of deviations from an average score, is that the range and standard deviation of scores of different tests differ. Data from intelligence tests may be used to illustrate the difficulties that arise.

The same test sometimes has fluctuations in the standard deviation of scores at different ages, owing to errors of standardization. These affect in particular scores which deviate markedly from the mean. Thus, the 1937 revision of the Stanford-Binet scale, perhaps the most elaborately standardized intelligence test ever devised, has standard deviations which vary from 13 points at the age of 6 years to 20 points at the age of 12. An I.Q. of 74 points achieved by a 6-year-old child on this test is in consequence equivalent to an I.Q. of 60 achieved by a 12-year-old on the same test. Though TERMAN and MERRILL (1937) note the difference in the standard deviations at different ages they do not make corrections for size of standard deviation in the tables of I.Q.s given at the back of their book. It has been left to their colleague Professor MCNEMAR (1942) to publish the "corrected" I.Q.s for children of different ages. This he does in a technical discussion which is unknown to many of the psychologists and doctors who use the test as a diagnostic tool for the discovery of mental subnormality.

Uncertainties regarding the meaning of a score or record obtained from inadequately standardized data thus add to the difficulty of making an assessment of mental subnormality. The samples on which tests are standardized are also in many cases not representative ones, and serious bias enters into many of the published norms of behaviour or intelligence because of sampling errors. Both the Gesell norms and the Binet test have been criticized on this score.

3. Even if there were scales for measuring subnormality which were absolutely reliable—in the sense that there would be perfect agreement among qualified observers or different test scores as to

each person's standing on the scale—prediction of subsequent performance might still be very fallible. A diagnostic estimate of present mental functioning gives us only one point on a curve of growth and development. The slope of this curve is not the same for all individuals. This is generally recognized; but the extent to which performance fluctuates over a period of time has received less publicity, in spite of the fact that two summaries of the literature cite between three and four hundred research studies published up to 1940 which have a bearing on this problem. (NEMZIK, 1933; THORNDIKE, 1940.) Typical of the findings obtained in longitudinal studies of intelligence quotients obtained by testing and retesting the same individuals are the results of HONZIK, MACFARLANE and ALLEN (1948). These show that scores on tests given to children under 2 years of age have little or no relation to scores obtained during school age or adolescence. Tests given to children of 2 years of age predict performance at the age of 5 to an extent little better than chance ($r = 0.32$). Though the prediction of subsequent performance on mental tests does increase with the age at which the first test is given, prediction remains hazardous. If we consider the extent of changes in I.Q. for the age period of 6 to 18 years, for example, we find that nearly 60 per cent of a group change 15 points or more; the I.Q.s of 33 per cent of the group change 20 or more points: and the I.Q.s of 9 per cent of the group change 30 or more points. Only 15 per cent of the group change less than 10 points of I.Q. HONZIK, MACFARLANE and ALLEN conclude that "A prediction based on a six-year test would be wrong to the extent of 20 I.Q. points for one out of three children by the age of 18 years, and to the extent of 15 I.Q. points for approximately six out of ten children".*

The popular notion that the I.Q. remains constant throughout

---

* The number of children whose I.Q.s fluctuate widely is probably greater in this investigation than would be found in a similar study carried out today. This is in part because the corrections for size of standard deviation were not adequate, and in part because early versions of the Binet test were more imperfect measuring instruments than are more recently devised tests. HONZIK, MACFARLANE and ALLEN's investigation is nonetheless of great importance because it shows the true extent of the error of prediction of the I.Q. at the time when the doctrine of the constancy of the I.Q. was largely unchallenged. This doctrine has had a profound effect on psychological thinking about mental deficiency, and its influence in this field still remains strong.

life is thus seriously misleading, and similar unreliability of prediction obtains elsewhere. Physical growth is by no means even
and continuous, though the effects of serious injury or defect in
early childhood on subsequent growth or development may be
predictable with considerable accuracy. Subnormality definable
only in educational social or occupational terms is much more
subject to change.

4. In many of the longitudinal studies which have been carried
out to examine the constancy of the I.Q., environmental conditions
have remained more or less the same throughout the period of
study. Children living in their own homes usually live under conditions which do not vary very greatly over a period of years. Some
studies have, however, been made of the effects of environmental
stimulation on mental-test performance. Most work on this aspect
of mental growth has been concerned mainly with changes in the
amount of cognitive stimulation. Perhaps the most striking example of the effect of environment has been given by KLINEBERG
(1940) who has shown that the intelligence quotients of negro
children living in the more liberal northern States of the U.S.A.
are on the average higher than those of white children living in the
south, despite the discrimination and restriction still operating
against them. The mean I.Q. of samples of American negro children is a function of their cultural emancipation.

Recently attention has been drawn to the importance of environmental factors in influencing the I.Q. of certified defectives. An
outstanding study is that by CLARKE and CLARKE (1953) who also
review the literature. CLARKE and CLARKE report that adolescents
and adults who come into a mental institution from a home
environment which is "very bad", as assessed by 12 clearly defined
criteria, show substantial rises (a mean of 10 points) in I.Q. during
the relatively short period of two years after admission, whereas
those who come from environments which are less bad show only
the increase which would be expected on immediate retest.
Changes in I.Q. in the group coming from "very bad" homes
ranged up to 25 points, and it is obvious that many of the incre-
ments which occurred over this time interval did not represent the
total increment which the individual had already made or would
make in the future. HONZIK and her collaborators (1948) have

shown that some normal children show consistent upward or downward trends in I.Q. over periods of many years, and they report changes of up to 50 I.Q. points. Though similar studies with defectives have been carried out in the past, the numbers of cases have been small and the statistical and experimental controls inadequate. The study by CLARKE and CLARKE is free from the weaknesses of the earlier studies.

It is to be expected that within the next few years our knowledge of this matter will change very considerably. Today we know only enough to make us cautious in our diagnosis of mental sub-normality and unwilling to make dogmatic predictions as to the future performance of individuals regarded as subnormal.

5. Discussion so far has been concerned solely with the relia-bility and validity of measurements of single aspects of function. But mental deficiency is not a clinical entity, and, as was men-tioned above, diagnosis is made on the basis of many criteria. Between the different criteria used the correlations tend to be low, so that a person judged grossly subnormal in one aspect of be-haviour would often not be judged so in others. Intellectual and temperamental qualities, for example, are not closely associated with each other; nor is school success necessarily a good predictor of occupational adjustment. Even where there is a close association between different indices of function as is the case between intelligence-test scores and academic success (for many intelligence tests are constructed in order to predict school success), the pre-diction of one measure from the other will still be very inaccurate in individual cases.

6. Finally, and in many ways most important, what constitutes subnormality is to a very large extent socially determined by the thresholds of community tolerance, as McCULLOUGH (1947) has pointed out. These are so subject to change in the light of changing social and economic circumstances that even the most accurate and sensitive diagnostic tools are not likely to be able to predict with accuracy whether one and the same person in different social circumstances will be classifiable as mentally subnormal.

Thus we cannot tell from cross-section studies how many of those who are judged subnormal as adults might have been judged normal as children, or how many subnormal children grow up into adults who are regarded as normal. Nor can we tell from surveys how many adults who are socially incompetent during periods of heavy unemployment would have been so under conditions of full employment, or how many socially incompetent persons in rural areas would have been above the threshold of community tolerance in urban areas and vice versa. We do know from longitudinal studies that the changes in functioning are very considerable, and we can deduce from prevalence rates obtained in cross-section surveys that the proportions of the population of different age-groups who are regarded as mentally defective differ greatly. These two points—the dependence of the diagnosis on the age at which the condition is diagnosed and the influence of socio-economic conditions in determining whether the diagnosis is made at all—should be borne in mind, however, in considering the surveys that have actually been carried out.

Assessments of the Prevalence of Mental Deficiency

Surveys of mental deficiency have been of two main sorts: psychometric studies; and field studies, which have usually employed both intelligence tests and clinical techniques. A third type of study relevant to the matter of prevalence is the follow-up study of individuals classified as subnormal during one period or other of their lives. These three types will be briefly discussed.

Psychometric Studies of Mental Subnormality

Much of the confusion regarding intelligence quotients has been cleared up by WECHSLER (1944), whose book on adult intelligence gives a lucid summary of the controversies. If we accept his conclusion that intelligence-test scores are statistical concepts, it follows that they will be valuable as diagnostic tools for the discovery of mental subnormality chiefly for rough screening purposes. A commonly accepted criterion of intellectual inadequacy so great as to make probable the diagnosis of mental subnormality is a score on a suitable intelligence test which falls more than two standard deviations below the mean. Below this point, in a normal distribution, 2·27 per cent of cases will fall. We may, if we wish, decide that an individual, in order to be classified as subnormal, must obtain a score of more than two standard deviations below the

mean on some appropriate intelligence test. This is administratively convenient, and has clinical justification since subnormal
people who need special care will require supervision, treatment,
and control which is likely to differ in important ways from that
which people of normal or superior intelligence may require. But
it tells us little about the prevalence of mental deficiency.

Surveys which have depended only on intelligence-test findings
can therefore be dismissed briefly. PENROSE (1949) has given a
summary of some of the most important studies. As might be
expected, the results are not very consistent.

"BINET and SIMON (1907) quoted the findings of a minis-
terial commission in France which reported 1 per cent of
boys and 0·9 per cent of girls to be defective. They also
mentioned that other authorities had given much higher
estimates: VANEY suggested 2–4 per cent and THAMIN and
ABADIE 5 per cent for the proportion of defective children of
school age.

"American estimates, based on the testing of school-
children, usually have varied between 2 and 3 per cent.
Naturally much depends upon definitions. As YERKES (1921)
pointed out, according to a current definition that anyone
with a mental age of 12 years or less was defective, almost half
the white males drafted into the American army in 1917 must
have been defective. If, however, a mental age of 8 were taken
as the limit, less than 2 per cent would fall into the defective
group. Of the children entering school for the first time in
Massachusetts, 2·6 per cent were considered to be defective
and 11·2 per cent retarded though not defective, by DAYTON
(1939). The figures are liable to differ widely in different
States or localities. The Scottish Survey (1933) led to an
opinion that more than 1·5 per cent but not so many as 3 or
4 per cent of school-children were to be found in the mentally
defective category. DAHLBERG (1937) estimated that 3 per
cent of boys and 1·7 per cent of girls in Sweden required
education in special classes for the mentally defective."

Recent Scandinavian studies have been summarized by FREM-
MING (1951); they give results consistent with those mentioned
above. A very large study has recently been completed in France

(HEUYER, 1950) which, using a special scoring and scaling technique for a group test administered to a very large sample of children, arrived at prevalence rates which varied from $1\frac{1}{2}$ per cent to 11 per cent of schoolchildren depending on age; and German, American, and Swiss work exists.

The prevalence rates given in all of these studies illustrate the uncertainty of the diagnosis. Estimates are either made rigidly on the basis of some arbitrary I.Q. figure—often without making corrections for the size of the standard deviation or the nature of the test—or on the other hand are reflections of the amount of special provision either available or recommended in the communities in which the studies were made. Very few writers have been aware of the nature of the assumptions they have made in carrying out large-scale testing. A notable exception has been Sir CYRIL BURT (1922) who more than 30 years ago suggested I.Q. thresholds for mental subnormality in regard to London children which were based on the amount of special school accommodation available at the time.

Field Studies

More comprehensive studies using criteria from a number of sources have been made by a number of investigators who have carried out field studies. A few of the prevalence rates arrived at by former investigators are quoted in the English survey known as the Wood Report (1929). They are given in the following tabulation:

Year	Investigation	Estimated number of mentally deficient, per 1,000 of population
1906	Royal Commission	4·61
1915	New York State Commission	4·13
1915	W. E. Fernald	4·00
1915	Porter County (Indiana Survey)	7·35
1916	Newcastle County (Delaware Survey)	3·82
1916	C. H. Strong's investigation of New York charities	3·40
1916	Nassau County (New York Survey)	5·44

The Report comments that it is "so difficult to compare the conditions and standards of these investigations . . . that it would be an unprofitable task to attempt a detailed discussion of these various estimates".

The Wood Report is itself the most thorough and best known of all studies that have been carried out. An investigation was made of six representative areas in England and Wales, having in all a population of over 600,000. They included three urban and three rural areas. The survey was carried out by a single medical investigator, Dr. E. O. LEWIS, who had also been a teacher. He was particularly well-qualified to make his clinical assessments.

For the investigation of schoolchildren a threefold process of selection was employed. The headmaster or class master was asked to select the 15 per cent of each age-group in his school who were considered the most backward. This group was examined with group intelligence tests, and the children who secured the lowest number of marks on these were examined individually by the medical investigator. The individual examination consisted chiefly of the application of intelligence and educational tests, and a routine physical examination. 6 per cent of children in infants' departments of the schools were examined individually, as were all children with paralysis or epilepsy or those who were "abnormal temperamentally". Special attempts were made to visit children who did not attend school, either because they were too young, of too low a mental grade, or because they had left school but not yet attained the age of 16 years. Their names were obtained from the local mental-deficiency authorities, the officers of the child welfare clinics, health visitors (public-health nurses), and district nurses. Children not at school because they were over school age were brought to notice by head teachers.

The investigation of adults proved a more difficult task, and Dr. LEWIS had to rely on a large number of sources, some statutory, some voluntary. The Local Authority under the Mental Deficiency Acts, 1913 to 1927, the Local Education Authority, the Poor Law Authority, the Medical Officer of Health and other medical authorities, charitable institutions and homes, shelters and common lodging houses, the clergy—these were some of the sources of information. Systematic mental testing was not possible with the vast majority of adults ascertained in this investigation. Lower-grade cases were comparatively straightforward; but the borderline cases had to be approached with great tact. Many borderline cases were excluded because of lack of sufficiently definite evidence to justify their inclusion among the ascertained mentally deficient. The survey was thus incomplete as far as adults were concerned, but contained all the cases who could with certainty be included in the category.

On the basis of his findings, Dr. LEWIS concluded that just under 1 per cent of the population could be classified as mentally defective. The incidence was found to be considerably higher in rural than in urban areas. (Selective migration to the towns was believed to be the main factor responsible for the higher incidence in rural areas.)

Several conclusions were to be drawn from LEWIS's study.

First, of every 100 mentally defective persons, it was estimated that approximately 75 were feeble-minded, 20 imbeciles, and only 5 of idiot grade. In other words, the greatest proportion of the subnormal were of mild grade and potentially capable of being taught to make a fairly adequate social adjustment in certain circumstances. Other investigators have also found that the proportion of mild subnormality greatly outweighs that of more severe cases.

Secondly, the prevalence of mental deficiency varied greatly according to the different age-groups. Few children of less than 7 years of age were diagnosed as mentally defective; during the period of school age the incidence of diagnosed subnormality rose sharply; and in adulthood the proportion certifiable as mentally defective again dropped.

A third conclusion reached by Dr. LEWIS was that, contrary to general belief, the rural defective adult is a more conspicuous failure than the urban. In the country, people work alone during the greater part of the time. Hence they must have initiative and independence—at least where farming is highly mechanized, as in England. This conclusion, which may not be true of all countries, should serve as a warning against the complacent attitude sometimes adopted towards the rural defective, and dispose of the argument that in countries where agriculture uses twentieth-century techniques farm work is the ideal occupation for the simple-minded. (It may be added that similar arguments could be applied to domestic service for women.)

Very similar findings have been obtained by LEMKAU, TIETZE and COOPER (1942), who carried out a smaller survey of mental health problems in the Eastern Health District of Baltimore (population 55,000). If LEWIS's data and the Baltimore data are compared the two sets of figures show a common pattern of variation by age, showing a peak prevalence between the ages of 10 and 14 years, and falling off sharply above and below these ages. In LEWIS's estimates the total population showed a prevalence of 8·6 per 1,000 of the general population and in the Baltimore study 12·2 per 1,000.

Table 3. Distribution of Mental Defectives by Age, per 1,000 of the General Population, in Two Surveys

Age in years	SURVEY England & Wales*	Baltimore†
0– 4	1·2	·7
5– 9	15·5	11·8
10–14	25·6	43·6
15–19	10·8	30·2
20–29	8·4	7·6
30–39	5·7	8·2
40–49	5·4	7·4
50–59	4·9	4·5
60 and over	2·9	2·2
All age-groups	8·6	12·2

* Based on data from the Wood Report.
† Based on data from LEMKAU, TIETZE & COOPER.

The Baltimore investigators comment that the large differences between children and adults cannot be explained by attributing them to the known higher death-rates among the mentally subnormal, since the decline with age is greatest among mild cases and smallest among the moderate and severe cases. If differential mortality were an important factor the opposite would be true, since death rates are highest among idiots and lowest among morons. Differences in definition and ease of case-finding are responsible.

The Wood Report and the Baltimore investigation are perhaps the two most thorough studies that have been made of populations large enough to enable conclusions of some general interest to be drawn. There are, however, a number of other studies which have been carried out, many of them in Scandinavia. FREMMING (1951), who has himself carried out an investigation on the Danish island of Bornholm, has given a useful review of the Scandinavian literature.

FREMMING in his own investigation distinguished between "mental defectives, whose development does not reach beyond that of an eleven-year-old child (I.Q. 70–75), and milder cases of retarded development whose I.Q. is above 75 but below 90". We may note here that on a test with a mean of 100 and a standard deviation of 15 or 16, no less than 25 per cent. of the population would have I.Q.s below 90 and nearly 5 per cent I.Q.s below 75. The value of the criterion of retarded development used by FREMMINGS is thus limited.

In addition, FREMMING took into account "the power of social adaptation no less than the results of intelligence tests". Since he used the biographical method, tracing the history of all the 4,130 persons born on the island between 1883–87 for whom information could be procured up to 1939, when the investigation was begun, he was unable to make extensive use of intelligence tests; he relied instead partly on psychiatric examinations conducted in the home, and partly on information collected from relatives, doctors, school-masters, employers, or local welfare officials. His criteria were mixed, and, as he was concerned with the expectation of mental infirmity rather than with the prevalence at any one time, his findings are not strictly comparable with those mentioned earlier. Some interesting results of this investigation of a rural area do, however, emerge.

There were 55 mentally subnormal persons among the 4,130 included in the total sample. The frequency was thus 1·33 per cent ±0·18 per cent. More than three-fourths were morons. Those of imbecile grade had been cared for in public institutions and had been incapable of serious work. The idiots had died young. Just over half of the morons were in public institutions or receiving public relief. All were described as slow, inferior workers, none had been able to keep up with fellow-pupils at school, few could calculate, and some were illiterate.

For comparison, FREMMING gives the results of similar investigations carried out elsewhere. The prevalence rates differ considerably.

By a genealogical investigation STRÖMGREN (1938) found 0·70 per cent mentally defective individuals in a sample of the Danish population; but by using the census method the figure was raised to 3·12 per cent. In Finland, M. KAILA (1942) carried out a comprehensive investigation according to the census method. Among the adult population he found 0·44 per cent mentally subnormal, but in the age-group 10–14 years, which was closely investigated, he found 1·2 per cent. In Sweden, TORTSEN SJÖGREN (1948) determined the frequency of mental subnormality by a genetic-statistical and psychiatric survey of a limited rural area (9,000 persons). He found the expectation to be 0·8 per cent ±0·10 per cent. FREMMING claims that the results of these and other Scandinavian investigations are fairly similar; they give the figure for certifiable mental deficiency as 1–1½ per cent of the population. But, as was pointed out above, there is little value in giving an overall figure of the prevalence of mental deficiency in view of the large differences found in different age-groups. Rather, each age-group should be considered separately.

Follow-up Studies

Follow-up studies of adults who as children or young persons were classified as mentally subnormal provide a third source of information about the prevalence of mental subnormality. Many such investigations have been carried out, particularly in the United States of America. The proportion of mentally subnormal children who grow up into essentially normal adults is always high, varying from about one-half to three-quarters in most studies. Investigations carried out since the war under conditions of full employment have resulted in figures which are higher than those given in pre-war studies when there was mass unemployment.

Typical of these studies is an investigation carried out by BALLER

(1936) in 1935 of a group of 206 adults who as children had been classified as mentally subnormal, and continued by CHARLES (1953) fifteen years after. BALLER found that at the time he made his enquiries more than 80 per cent of the sample were self-supporting, though 60 per cent had had some relief during the depression years. CHARLES also found 83 per cent of the sample self-supporting, the range of occupations being from "managerial positions to unskilled labour". The proportion needing relief of some sort from the State or from social agencies declined with each successive period after the depression, showing that the subjects were able to take advantage of improving economic conditions. They were on the average 42 years of age at the time CHARLES carried out his study in 1950.

Of the sample, 80 per cent were married, and 80 per cent of these had children. The number of children per family was slightly less than the national average, and they formed a representative sample of the general population of children (mean I.Q. = 95; standard deviation = 16 points). In short, though about 20 per cent of the subjects were in institutions or under the care of their parents, the remainder of these persons who as children had been certified as mentally deficient on clinical, educational, and psychometric grounds were able to live independent lives which differed little if at all from those lived by "normal" adults.

This study and the many others of its kind fully bear out the statement made earlier that it is quite false to think of feeblemindedness as something fixed and incurable. It is, rather, an administrative concept and as such is related to the conditions and facilities available in the community.

Discussion

Under the term "mentally defective", two types of individuals are included. One type, as KANNER (1947) has pointed out, consists of individuals "so markedly deficient in their cognitive, emotional and constructively conative potentialities that they would stand out as defectives in any existing culture. . . . The other type is made up of individuals whose limitations are definitely related to the standards of the particular culture which surrounds them. In less complex, less intellectually centred societies they would have no trouble in attaining and retaining equality . . . and, some might

c

even be capable of gaining superiority by virtue of assets other than those measured by intelligence tests." But as soon as scholastic curricula demand "competition in spelling, history, geography, long division and other preparations deemed essential for the tasks of feeding chickens, collecting garbage and wrapping bundles in a department store," their shortcomings appear during their school life. These cases are termed the "feeble-minded".

In highly-developed countries the proportion of the general population who suffer from moderate or severe mental defect is probably about three per thousand, if the Wood Report figures are representative. Their average life-span is shorter than that of the general population. KAPLAN (1939) reported that the average life-span of 768 imbeciles and idiots was 26·6 years for imbeciles and 19 years for idiots; and DAYTON (1931) found the death rate for idiots five times, and that for imbeciles two-and-a-half times, that of the general population. Mongols, who form the most common of the clinical types, occur approximately three times in every two thousand births. Their mortality is high, but their life expectancy, until recently about 12 years, has probably been increased considerably by recent advances in medicine.

We can expect in the future that morbidity and mortality tables will be made available for each of the other clinical types; and, as our knowledge increases, the incidence rates of moderate and severe defect will become better known. Overall figures for patients by grade are helpful only for the planning of services.

All the evidence indicates that the number of feeble-minded persons is much greater than the number of moderate and severe cases. Their disabilities are educational and social rather than pathological, and for the most part they exist only in relation to certain types of society. At the present time the proportion of school-leavers who need special placement in jobs and special supervision is perhaps 0·5 per cent. The number decreases as adolescents grow to maturity. How many need institutional care can be determined only in relation to alternative provisions open to them and their parents, to the amount of unemployment, the social welfare services, and the vocational guidance and training they receive. It is quite possible that a healthy society, even if highly industrialized, might find only a very small number of feeble-minded persons who require special care, at least in adult-hood.

At the present time, the proportion of children considered educationally subnormal in different countries varies from about 1 per cent to 4 per cent; a further 6 per cent to 9 per cent are so dull as to require special assistance within the normal school system. But the number ascertained as educationally subnormal, and found in need of special educational treatment because of their subnormality, also depends to a large extent on the size and nature of classes in the schools, the facilities available to the teacher, and the training and competence of the teacher. If classes were small enough there would be few children who required special educational provision because of educational subnormality.

Prevalence surveys of mental deficiency have differed in many ways. They are alike in one respect: all have revealed a much higher prevalence of subnormality than any society is known to make provision for. In particular, the needs of infants and pre-school children have been overlooked and it is evident that much uncared for mental defect must exist among children of pre-school age. Considered from the point of view of developing a comprehensive programme to meet the needs of the subnormal, it is probable that energetic attempts to diagnose mental subnormality at an early age would lead to the discovery of many more cases during the pre-school years. To give suitable treatment and guidance to these during childhood would impose new responsibilities on the maternal and child health services and on the educational authorities. But, as a direct result of the special care during childhood, there would probably be a marked decrease in the number of cases who required special care during their adult life.

The observations of the World Health Organisation Joint Expert Committee on the Physically Handicapped Child (1952) are relevant to this matter. The committee drew a useful distinction between the terms "primary" prevention and "secondary" prevention.

> "Primary prevention relates to measures which prevent the initial occurrence of physical handicap—for example, the control of tuberculosis. Secondary prevention relates to early discovery, early diagnosis, and early and continuous medical

treatment and rehabilitation, so that the extent of the impact of the disability will be mitigated as much as possible.''

The need for the primary prevention of mental deficiency does not require stressing—though the amount of money spent on research into primary prevention is still small. The importance of the secondary preventive services has nowhere been fully realized.

CHAPTER THREE

THE MENTAL DEFICIENCY SERVICES TODAY

RESPONSIBILITY for the care and education of the mentally subnormal and mentally defective is today divided mainly between the Health and Education Authorities, both local and national. The education of children who are considered "educable" is the joint responsibility of the Ministry of Education and the Local Education Authorities, as is the education of normal children. "Ineducable" children* are referred by the Education Authority to the Local Health Authority which has the responsibility (*a*) for "providing suitable supervision for such defectives, and if this affords insufficient protection, taking steps to secure that they are sent to institutions or placed under guardianship; (*b*) providing suitable training or occupation for defective under supervision or guardianship; (*c*) making provision for the guardianship of defectives placed under guardianship by orders under the Act." †

Children in institutions are provided for by the Health Service, and no charge is made for their stay in hospital either to the families or to the Local Authorities. Adult defectives who become "subject to be dealt with" may be either placed under statutory supervision or under guardianship, thereby remaining the responsibility of the Local Health Authorities; alternatively they too may be placed in institutions under the Health Service.

The transfer of the responsibility for providing institutional accommodation from the Local Authorities to the Minister of Health has resulted in important changes in the distribution of hospital beds. Where Local Authorities in the past made adequate provision for defectives, some of this has now been allocated to

---

* These are, on the one hand, imbeciles and idiots, and on the other hand, children called feeble-minded, or "detrimental" because they suffer from a disability of mind which makes it "inexpedient that they should be educated in association with other children" owing to faulty habits or behaviour.

† Guardianship differs from statutory supervision in that a defective under guardianship may be placed in a private family other than his own, and the parents or guardians may be paid for his maintenance, clothing and so on if he is unable to meet all of these expenses.

other areas which had previously made few beds available; these latter now have an opportunity in some cases to place larger numbers of defectives in hospital. This change, which resulted from the coming into force of the National Health Service Act in 1948, is likely to have two important effects upon ascertainment and disposal of mental defectives. The number of defectives ascertained by some of those Local Health Authorities which have in the past reported few cases, is bound in time to increase enormously, since institutional provision is now more likely to be obtained, and at no direct cost to themselves. Secondly, there is a danger that Local Authorities may recommend institutional care for some defectives who might otherwise be a charge on the rates, even though from a national standpoint the social costs of keeping them in the community might well be less than the cost of keeping them in institutions. The position of the mental-deficiency services today is an unstable one.

The actual numbers under different forms of care are given in Table 4.

Table 4. Numbers of Mental Defectives Receiving Some Form of Care on 31st December, 1954

In mental deficiency institutions and homes (including 4,884 patients on licence)	60,868
Under supervision or guardianship (i.e. under care by local health authorities)	76,987
Total	137,855

These numbers do not of course include the educationally subnormal who are dealt with by the education authorities.

Further information about the main classes of the mentally subnormal is as follows.

Educationally Subnormal Children

The education of educationally subnormal children is the responsibility of the education authorities. The Ministry of Education reported that in December 1954 there were 22,895 children in special schools for the educationally subnormal, while 12,578 were on waiting lists.

The total number of children actually ascertained in 1954 as being in need of education in special schools (35,473) is, however, a serious understatement of the numbers thought to need it. These have been officially estimated as being 1·2 per cent of the children of school age, and since the number of children of compulsory school age is approximately six million, the number of places required on this estimate cannot be much less than 72,000, even allowing for the fact that many educationally subnormal children are not ascertained until they have been at school for a year or two. For children who are later deemed "ineducable" may be tried in special schools; and special school children may remain at school for one, and occasionally for more than one year longer than do normal children. The number of children ascertained is thus about half the number presumed to exist, and the amount of accommodation available is less than one-third of the amount considered necessary.*

Idiot, Imbecile and Feeble-Minded Children

Statistical information about children excluded from special schools because of their mental subnormality is inadequate, and no recent attempt has been made to review the position. In the absence of more recent data the Wood Report statistics must form the basis for estimating the numbers of ineducable children in England and Wales today.

Lewis estimated the prevalence rate of idiocy and imbecility among children of school age as approximately 4·24 per thousand. There is more reason to accept this estimate than any of the other Wood Report statistics, since, as has been pointed out, the survey of children was more thoroughly carried out than the survey of adults, and the criteria of diagnosis of idiocy and imbecility were more easily definable than was that of feeble-mindedness. If we accept LEWIS's figures there are today more than 25,000 ineducable children of compulsory school age, and a total of 42,400 idiot and

---

* The Ministry of Education (1945) estimate that in addition to the 1·2 per cent of educationally subnormal children who need education in special schools, a further 9 or 10 per cent need education in special classes in ordinary schools. No recent information is available as to the number of such special classes that exist. It is known, however, that provision falls far short of the 600,000 places considered necessary.

imbecile children aged o to 16 years. Of these only 5,000 are in hospitals or institutions and the remainder are in the community.

Some of these children attend occupation centres or special clubs. There were 255 centres in December 1954 as compared with 183 centres and 12 clubs in 1950, and the number of children on the registers of centres was 7,150 as compared with a total of 6,318 in 1950. How many more children could profit from the kind of training given in occupation centres and what provision is made for them in the absence of organized facilities is not accurately known. Table 5 gives the figures supplied by local health authorities of the numbers both of children and of adults considered suitable for and actually receiving training in December 1954.

Table 5. * *Mental Defectives suitable for and receiving Training at Local Health Authority Centres and at Home, at 31st December, 1954*

	Suitable	Receiving
Under 16		
Occupation centres (all types)	10,122	7,150
Home training	777	639
	10,899	7,789
16 and over		
Occupation centres (all types)	8,747	3,792
Home training	1,891	1,091
	10,638	4,883
All ages	21,537	12,672

Adults

Little information is available about adult defectives "ascertained" but remaining in the community. No comprehensive data are published as to their distribution by sex, age, grade, social class of family, and occupation, if any. Nor would it be possible to obtain this information except as a result of inquiry from the 146 Local Health Authorities in the country. It is generally believed, on the basis of the Wood Committee's figures and comparable data, that whereas severe mental defect is to be found among all

* From Report of the Ministry of Health 1954. (Part 1.)

social classes in roughly equal incidence, high-grade mental defect is more common among social classes IV and V in the Registrar General's classification, than among the higher classes. If the criterion of mental deficiency in adulthood is the need to seek assistance of the public authorities because a person is unable to fend for himself, and has no relatives who provide the necessary care, it is likely that this will be true. To disentangle the biological from the social factors that contribute to this state of affairs is, however, a more difficult problem, and one to which no definitive answer can be given. It will not be discussed here.

In December 1954 there were 7,033 defectives, of whom about half were children, on waiting lists of Regional Hospital Boards. The occupied bed space was 52,240. Since the "recognized" bed space in these institutions was 48,256 and there were 1,612 out of use (mainly owing to shortage of staff), the amount of over-crowding was 12 per cent. There was an overall shortage of 12,629 beds in relation to officially recognized needs. Though the number of beds is being increased, the shortage is still a serious one, and is likely to remain so.

Types of Institutional Care

Institutions for the mentally defective differ greatly in size, and, to some extent, in the type of patient they receive. Table 6 gives a frequency distribution of the number of institutions of various sizes and the proportion of the total number of patients they hold. It is compiled from statistics published by the Board of Control for the year 1946. Certain ambiguities in the date which have been discussed elsewhere (TIZARD, 1951b) make Table 6 inaccurate in some respects; the general picture is, however, believed to be a true one.

The figures for the two State Institutions, the 116 Certified Institutions, and the 99 Approved Institutions were first grouped by the writers in class intervals of 100, for institutions with more than 100 beds. The figures obtained were then regrouped into the larger class intervals shown here.

Over two-thirds of mentally defective patients are in institutions of more than 500 beds, and over one-half are in institutions of more than 1,000 beds. Public policy, as expressed in the Wood

Report and subsequently, still favours the setting up of institutions
with between one and two thousand beds. These are in most cases
"comprehensive" institutions or "colonies", taking both high-
grade and low-grade patients.

*Table 6. Number of patients in State and Certified Institutions, and
Institutions Approved under Section 37 of the Mental Deficiency Act,
September 1946**

Size of institution (beds)	No. of institutions of that size	Total* No. of patients in each category	Per cent of total No. of patients in all institutions
More than 2000	4	8900	17·38
1500–1999	3	5550	10·84
1000–1499	8	10100	19·72
500– 999	15	10150	19·82
100– 499	48	11500	22·45
50– 99	39	2925	5·71
25– 49	48	1776	3·47
1– 24	52	312	·61
Total	217	51213*	100·00

The reasons for the large size of mental-deficiency hospitals are
partly historical, partly economic. Some of the largest hospitals
were set up half a century ago and more as Poor Law Institutions,
and their architecture, and much of their equipment, reflect this
period of their history. But even modern hospitals may be large in
size for supposed reasons of economy. As a much-quoted passage
in the Wood Report says: "An institution which takes all grades
and types is economical because the high grade patients do the
work, and make everything necessary, not only for themselves, but
also for the lower grade. In an institution taking only lower grades
the whole of the work has to be done by paid staff; in one taking
only higher grades the output is greater than is required for the
institution itself, and there is difficulty in disposing of it." An
additional reason, given in the Report of the Departmental Committee (1931), set up to discuss institutions for defectives, is that

* The figures given in this Table are estimates derived from the Board of
Control *List of State and Certified Institutions, Certified Houses, and Approved
Homes for Mental Defectives* (1946).

large institutions are more economical as far as medical staff are concerned. It is not practicable to have a doctor for a small number of patients and since the care of mental defectives has always been almost exclusively a medical concern (there are still very few psychologists or teachers employed in mental-deficiency practice though the number has grown recently) the size of the institution has of necessity been large.

Grade of Patients under Care

In the absence of published statistics from official sources it is useful to have an estimate of the numbers of adults of different grades in mental-deficiency hospitals. Statistics compiled by PENROSE (1949) based on his Colchester Survey (PENROSE, 1938) enable an estimate to be given of the proportions in one large and representative mental-deficiency hospital during the 'thirties.

It can be inferred from his data that 53 per cent of adult patients were feeble-minded, and that the majority of these were young adults, aged between 16 and 30 years of age. If an I.Q. of 40 points is taken as the upper limit of imbecile intelligence, the proportion of feeble-minded and dull adults in PENROSE'S sample rises to 66·7 per cent, two-thirds of the total adult sample.

A Survey of Hospital Patients

More recent and comprehensive information about patients in institutions was obtained by us in a survey which was carried out between November 1951 and February 1952 of a 5-per-cent sample of patients on the books of mental-deficiency institutions in three of the Home Counties. The survey was concerned with the sex, age, grade, type of nursing and rewards and occupations of the patients. (O'CONNOR and TIZARD, 1954.)

Population and Sample

The population from which the 5-per-cent sample was drawn consisted of patients in all hospitals in the counties of Kent, London and Surrey, which in 1946 had been classified by the Board of Control as Certified Institutions, or Institutions approved under Section 37 of the Mental Deficiency Acts. Approximately 100 patients housed in Approved Homes in Surrey and Kent were excluded from the survey, which covered all other institutions in the selected area.

The size of the sample by hospitals is given in Table 7 below. The population from which the sample was drawn consisted of approximately 11,850 patients, more than one fifth of the total number of institutional defectives in England and Wales. Only patients detained under the Mental Deficiency Acts were included in the survey.

Table 7. Hospitals and Institutions Visited, with Size of Sample, by Sex

Hospital	Male	Female	Total
Botleys Park	43	37	80
Darenth Park	61	40	101
Farmfield	12	—	12
Fountain Hospital	15	17	32
Leavesden Hospital	33	40	73
Leybourne Grange Colony	28	35	63
Leytonstone House Hospital	1	17	18
Manor Hospital	36	39	75
Princess Christian's Farm Colony	4	6	10
Royal Earlswood Institution	19	11	30
St. Lawrence's Hospital	49	42	91
St. Theresa's Home	—	7	7
Totals	301	291	592

Method

In each hospital the sample was selected by drawing every twentieth name from a nominal roll of patients on the books, listed alphabetically. Case records and Orders were examined. Additional information was obtained by questioning senior members of the nursing staff. Patients between 16 and 29 years of age who were classified as feeble-minded, and who were not on licence or on leave were tested by the investigators on the Progressive Matrices Tests, in groups, but without a time limit. Between one and three days were spent at each hospital.

Results

1. *Distribution of patients by sex, age, and grade*—The number of patients of various ages by sex and grade is given in Table 8.

Table 8. Distribution of Patients by Sex, Age, and Grade

Sex and grade	Male				Female				Totals			
	c	b	a	T	c	b	a	T	c	b	a	T
Age 0–4	2	4	0	6	1	4	0	5	3	8	0	11
5–9	5	12	3	20	5	6	2	13	10	18	5	33
10–14	4	6	3	13	2	5	2	9	6	11	5	22
15	0	3	1	4	1	2	0	3	1	5	1	7
Total (Children)	11	25	7	43	9	17	4	30	20	42	11	73
16–19	1	12	17	30	1	9	13	23	2	21	30	53
20–29	3	33	42	78	4	27	30	61	7	60	72	139
30–39	2	24	37	63	2	17	39	58	4	41	76	121
40–49	1	15	38	54	0	26	41	67	1	41	79	121
50 +	0	13	20	33	1	29	22	52	1	42	42	85
Total (Adults)	7	97	154	258	8	108	145	261	15	205	299	519
Total	18	122	161	301	17	125	149	291	35	247	310	592

(Where Grade c =idiot; b =imbecile; a =feeble-minded person; T = total. Age is given as from last birthday. The number of patients aged 15 years is given separately in order that the number of children (aged 0–15) and of adults (aged 16 +) can be calculated.)

Forty-three patients or 8 per cent were admitted under Sections 8 or 9 of the Mental Deficiency Acts. The majority, 435, were admitted under other Sections. The data in Table 8 have been

arranged so that the number of "adults" and "children" appear
separately. (Persons over 16 years of age are classified as adults,
in accordance with common mental deficiency practice.)

Table 9. Per cent of all adult patients by age and grade $(N=519)$

Age	Grade			
	c	b	a	Total
16–29	2	15	20	37
30–39	1	8	15	24
40–49	—	8	15	23
50 +	—	8	8	16
Total	3	39	58	100

c =idiot; b =imbecile; a =feeble-minded.

Children made up 12·33 per cent of the patients, and of these the
majority were of low grade. (The Report of the Ministry of Health
for the year 1949 gives the percentage of children in institutions in
England and Wales as 12 per cent, which agrees with the figure
obtained in the survey.)

There were 43 per cent more males than females among the
children. In Table 9 is given the percentage of adult patients by
grade and age. The most recent report by the hospital authorities
to the Board of Control was consulted in order to determine the
grade of each patient.

Of the adults, 58 per cent were classified as feeble-minded.
Most of these were under 50 years of age.

2. *Distribution of patients by type of nursing needed and behaviour*—There were 26 male patients and 28 female patients on resident licence from the institution (8·6 per cent of male patients and
9·6 per cent of females). In addition 21 patients (16 males and 5
females) were on daily licence. The distribution of patients by sex,
grade, and type of nursing needed is shown in Table 10.

Supplementary questions added something to the picture as far
as behaviour was concerned. Thus, only one male and one female
patient had attempted suicide during the previous year; 12 (2 per
cent) had been charged with stealing; 55 (9 per cent) had had one

Table 10. *Numbers of Patients by Grade and Type of Nursing needed*
(*on day of survey*)

	Grade			
	c	b	a	T
Chronic sick	1	9	11	21
Temporarily in hospital	0	3	4	7
Cot and chair cases	12	10	3	25
Low-grade ambulant	13	74	14	101
Open wards	0	75	154	229
Locked wards ("Special Supervision")	8	72	62	142
Hostel	0	0	6	6
On leave	0	0	1	1
Absconded	0	0	6	6
Resident licence	1	4	49	54
Total	35	247	310	592

or more clashes with staff or patients serious enough to be recorded in case notes; 18 (3 per cent) had absconded. Ten female patients had been pregnant, or had had V.D. at some time in their lives, and 16 of the male patients had histories of homosexuality, indecent assault, or indecent exposure. Some of the incidents listed as indecent assault in case papers or orders were of a trivial character and had occurred many years previously. Seventy-seven patients (13 per cent) were doubly incontinent, and a further 27 (5 per cent) eneuretic. Of 68 patients (11·5 per cent) who suffered from epilepsy, 17 were severe cases (suffering grand mal attacks once a fortnight or more), 14 moderate, and 37 mild. Many other patients were described on case sheets as being epileptic, but had had no attacks during the last year, or, in some cases, at any time during their stay in hospital.

There were marked differences in the proportion of patients in different hospitals who were in locked wards. No doubt the type of patient was in part responsible for this, but hospital policies appeared also to differ. Out of the 538 resident patients 75 (13 per cent) left the hospital grounds once or more on day parole during the month preceding the date of the survey (29 females, 46 males).

Of male patients 76 and of females 47 (25 per cent and 16 per cent respectively) went on leave during the previous year. Over two-thirds of these patients were on leave for less than three weeks.

Rewards to patients—The rewards given to patients varied some-what from hospital to hospital. For low-grade patients rewards consisted of sweets or cigarettes. High-grade patients usually had rewards paid partly in kind, partly in cash. The figures given in Table 11 refer to the cash value of the rewards, whether or not the patients received money, tokens to be exchanged at the canteen, or actual goods.

Table 11. *Cash Value of Rewards of Pocket Money paid to Patients resident in hospital, during week of survey*

Value in shillings	Number of patients	Per cent of total
1 or less	225	42
2	77	14
3	91	17
4	54	10
5	34	6
6 to 10	34	6
11 to 15	5	1
16 +	10	2
Not ascertained	8	2
Total	538*	100

Total disbursed to 530 patients—£70 18s. 6d.

For patients on either daily or resident licence the rewards represented total earnings. Those on licence, however, earned wages which were often in excess of the amount of pocket money allowed them. (Additional amounts, when deductions have been made for board and lodgings, are credited to patients' accounts.) Hospital policies differed in the extent to which they allowed patients on licence control over their own affairs, and wages earned by patients on licence, as well as the amount of money or goods they were given to spend or use during the week of the survey, also

* Total excludes 54 patients on resident licence.

varied greatly. Those employed in factories and as labourers earned higher wages than those engaged in domestic service. Table 12 gives the length of time patients had been on licence.

Table 12. *Duration of Licence of* 54 *Patients out of Hospital at Time of Survey*

Period on Licence	Daily Licence			Resident Licence		
	Male	Female	Total	Male	Female	Total
Less than 3 months	1	0	1	5	2	7
3 to 6 months	1	0	1	4	5	9
6 to 12 months	0	0	0	4	5	9
1 to 2 years	4	0	4	6	8	14
2 to 5 years	6	0	6	5	5	10
More than 5 years	1	1	2	2	3	5
No information	3	4	7	0	0	0
Total	16	5	21	26	28	54

Occupations of patients—The number of patients employed on different types of job both inside and outside the hospitals is given in Table 13. About 40 per cent of those on licence were employed in domestic service of one sort or other. Surprisingly few patients were sent on licence to factory work or were found to be employed on farms or gardens. (Possibly the sample of defectives on licence was too small to enable us to generalize about the kind of jobs done by patients on licence.)

In summary it may be said that about three-fifths of the adult defectives in the sample of institutional patients investigated were certified as feeble-minded persons. The great majority of them were able-bodied, and most of them were free from the severely disabling psychopathic disturbances which might be held to make permanent segregation from the community necessary. All but about 10 per cent of the feeble-minded adult patients were employed in some way or other. Out of 240 resident feeble-minded adults 51, or more than one-fifth, were working in hospital workshops, while a further 81, or one-third, were working in the wards or as domestic servants in the hospital. Nine per cent of the patients were on licence and just over 4 per cent in daily service.

D

Table 13. *Occupations of Patients during Week of Survey*

Type of occupation	Patients working in hospital				On licence		
	Grade						
	c	b	a	Total	Daily	Resident	Total
1. Farm or garden	o	9	19	28	6	2	8
2. Domestic service in hospital	o	8	27	35	o	6	6
3. Other domestic work (private, hotel or kitchen)	o	o	3	3	5	22	27
4. Labouring	o	6	4	10	5	4	9
5. Factory or laundry	o	8	11	19	2	6	8
6. Messenger or van boy, shop assistant	o	o	7	7	3	2	5
7. School or occupation centre	4	19	10	33	o	1	1
8. Occupational therapy	o	19	20	39	o	o	o
9. Ward work	o	57	54	111	o	o	o
10. Hospital workshop	o	16	51	67	o	o	o
11. No information	o	o	9	9	o	6	6
12. Unemployable	30	101	25	156	o	5	5
Total	34	243	240	517	21	54	75

c = idiot; b = imbecile; a = feeble-minded.

Representativeness of the Survey Findings

The number of patients included in the survey, nearly 12,000, make the findings of importance. We have, in addition, attempted to check the representativeness of the data obtained as far as England and Wales as a whole are concerned. On this matter, unfortunately, no strictly comparable information was available at the time of the survey; the latest, and in fact the only information possessed by the Board of Control at that time with regard to the division of patients by grade was that concerning long-stay patients for the year 1949 (i.e. those who were in institutions vested in the Ministry of Health on 1st January 1949 and who were remaining in them on 31st December of that year). These represented approximately 93 per cent of all patients on the books of those hospitals in December 1949.

The classification upon which the Board of Control figures are based is the sevenfold one contained in the *International Statistical Classification of Diseases, Injuries and Causes of Death* (1948). The categories are as follows: Idiocy, Imbecility, Moron, Borderline Intelligence, Mongolism, Other and unspecified types, All other diagnoses. The Board's statistical information is obtained from returns made by hospitals and institutions. These returns are based partly on the grade of the patient—idiocy, imbecility, and feeble-mindedness (or moronity)—partly on clinical type (e.g. mongolism), and partly on extraneous and sometimes irrelevant considerations which appear to have come as a result of misunderstanding of the questions asked, or to be due to inadequate explanation of what was wanted on the part of those who drew up the record cards from which this information was obtained.

Dr. REES THOMAS, Senior Medical Commissioner of the Board of Control, who kindly supplied the information given in this section, writes of the data: "In the category 'mongolism' we have no information beyond the diagnosis given. The category 'other and unspecified types' is equally unsatisfactory; of the 219 cases (20 male, 22 female, age 0–15) 216 are returned as mental deficiency N.O.S. or mental retardation N.O.S. (not otherwise specified). The heading 'All other diagnoses' (1,408 patients) has 41 separate categories, none of which relate to grading. Examples are: head injuries, convulsions, encephalitis, epilepsy, asocial personality, and cerebral spastic infantile paralysis. In none of these cases can we find any information which will permit us to give you a grading."

The most useful comparison between our London Survey data and the Board of Control census figures is probably that between the proportions of adults in each of the three main categories by grade. This is given in Table 14. Here mongols have been included among the imbeciles while the categories "other and unspecified types" and "all other diagnoses" have been grouped together under a separate heading.

Allowing for sampling errors and differences in the manner in which the data were collected, the agreement between the two sets

Table 14. Percentage of adult patients by grade as obtained in London Survey 1951–52, and by Board of Control census 1949 of long-stay patients

Grade	BOARD OF CONTROL CENSUS		Per cent of patients by grade found in London survey
	No. of cases	Per cent of patients by grade	
Idiot	1,721	4	3
Imbecile	14,809	33	39
Feeble-minded	27,122	60	58
Other	1,313	3	—
Total	44,965	100	100

of figures is remarkably close. It thus seems very likely that the London data are comparable with what is to be found elsewhere in the country as far as grade of patient is concerned.

A Birmingham Survey

A valuable survey of the nine mental-deficiency colonies in the Birmingham Region, containing over 5,000 patients, has recently been carried out by CROSS (1954). His findings complement and extend those obtained by us, and give detailed information about the disposition of nursing staff ward by ward, the accommodation available, and the age distribution and employment of patients, both within the hospital and on licence.

In the Birmingham Region the proportion of adults classed as feeble-minded, imbecile and idiot are 50, 47 and 3 respectively, as compared with 58, 39 and 3 in our study, and perhaps 60, 36 and 4 for the national average.

CROSS gives the following table to show percentage distributions by place of employment of adult patients resident in the hospital.

The proportions of patients in different types of work differ somewhat from those found in the London Region, but the differences in classification used and in the distribution of patients by

Table 15. *Percentage Distributions of Mental Defectives in the Birmingham Region by Place of Employment*

Place of Employment	Males	Females
On daily licence	6·9	8·2
Employed on wards	24·5	25·2
Employed elsewhere in hospital	45·0	41·1
Unemployed	20·1	22·7
Sick	3·2	1·8
On leave	·3	1·0
Total	100·0	100·0

grade are no doubt in part responsible. Strict comparison of the figures is not possible.

CROSS has an interesting discussion of the 281 male and 255 female patients in his survey who were on full licence. They included only 23 children, of whom 19 were imbeciles and the other four feeble-minded. Three-quarters of the adults were feeble-minded. The male adults on licence tended to be younger than the females—58 per cent of all females on licence were aged 35 years or over as compared with only 31 per cent of the males—while 30 per cent of the males and only 13 per cent of the females were between 15 and 24 years of age.

When the proportions of male and female patients who were on licence to certain licensees were considered, striking differences were found. Nearly three-quarters of the males, but only 44 per cent of the females were on licence to hospitals. CROSS concludes that employing authorities are more likely to accept responsibility for female patients than for males. Hospitals and private individuals employ females as domestic workers, while at the same time accepting responsibility for their supervision; however, since the main source of employment for males is labouring on farms, or in gardens or factories, they are not normally resident with their employers, but travel to work each day.

It would be interesting to survey in more detail these differences between male and female patients on licence—to obtain by interview with patients, relatives and employers, information about their attitudes and opinions, and to make an assessment of the quality of the patients' homes. More needs to be known also about wages paid and the length of time patients spend on licence before discharge. These two factors, rather than the demand of the labour market, might perhaps account for most of the differences between males and females on licence.

Intelligence of Feeble-Minded Adults in Institutions

Although mental deficiency is not to be equated with lack of intelligence, there is almost universal agreement that low intelligence, as measured by intelligence tests, is one criterion by which "arrested or incomplete development of mind" can be judged. The convention has grown up that individuals who have I.Q.s of between 70 and 85 points on standard intelligence tests are not to be considered as cognitively defective but, rather, as intellectually dull. This convention has been widely adopted in American state legislation and has found its way into the *International Statistical Classification of Diseases, Injuries and Causes of Death* (1948) published by the World Health Organisation. As already mentioned, it has not been generally appreciated that the magnitude of an I.Q. depends upon the standard deviation of the test used as well as on other factors;* but the lower limit of I.Q. which falls within the normal range in our present industrial environment is perhaps about two standard deviations less than the mean. Below this point lie between two-and-two and one-half per cent of the population, the simple-minded from whom the mentally defective are said to be drawn. Some investigators, including E. O. Lewis and Sir Cyril Burt, have adopted a more conservative standard in judging cognitive defect in adults; for them an I.Q. of 60 marks the upper limit of defective intelligence and only the unstable with I.Q.s of more than 60 points are considered those "hybrid" cases who go to swell the ranks of the feeble-minded. Other investigators have taken as a dividing line an I.Q. of 75 or even 80 points. But an I.Q. of 70 points on a test whose standard deviation is 15 points is usually considered a convenient dividing line. Because problems

---

* This point has been discussed elsewhere (Tizard, 1950, 1953*b*).

of training the very stupid are to some extent different from those of training individuals who are merely dull it is of some importance to determine the distribution of intelligence in institutional cases.

PENROSE (1938) in his Colchester investigation, found that of a total of 519 adults classified as feeble-minded 156, or 30·06 per cent, were dull rather than cognitively defective, using his criterion of I.Q. 70 as the point of division on the I.Q. scale. He used as his measure of intelligence a combination of the 1916 Stanford-Binet Scale and the Porteus Maze Test, in which scores on the Stanford Scale were weighted three times those on the Porteus. The standard deviation of this combination is not known. Neither test is particularly suitable for adults, nor has either been properly standardized on an adult population. Where both tests have been given to the same individuals correlations obtained have differed considerably (TIZARD, 1951a). It is therefore unprofitable to speculate as to the "true", value of PENROSE'S figures which, nonetheless, indicate that the number of dull, rather than cognitively defective, adults in mental-deficiency institutions during the 'thirties was substantial.*

Several investigations carried out since the war clarify the position as far as the adult feeble-minded in institutions are concerned. The results are given in some detail below:

(*a*) *Test scores of* 104 *consecutive admissions to Darenth Park*—In 1949 a battery of cognitive tests was given to a sample of feeble-minded adults in Darenth Park. The sample consisted of 104 patients, consecutive male admissions to the hospital over the preceding three years. Not included in the sample were (i) old men and imbeciles, (ii) those who had been transferred, discharged or sent on licence before they could be tested, and (iii) those suffering from gross complicating physical disabilities. The selection of patients was made by Dr. J. M. CRAWFORD, then Deputy Superintendent of Darenth Park. The mean age of the sample was 20·9 years, S.D. 4·6 years.

The mean I.Q.s and frequency distributions of I.Q.s on five intelligence tests are given in Table 16. The tests were: Kohs

---

* On the basis of a recent study carried out in one large mental-deficiency hospital, FITZPATRICK (1955) has concluded that there has not been a rise in the number of patients with high I.Q.s who are certified as feeble-minded—at least in that hospital.

Blocks (Alexander Version), Progressive Matrices, 1938 (given to small groups but without a time limit), the Binet Vocabulary sub-test of the 1937 Terman-Merrill Revision, the Porteus Maze Test (Vineland Revision), and Cattell's Non-Verbal Intelligence Test, Form IB. Fifty of the patients were given the full 1937 Terman-Merrill Revision of the Stanford Binet Scale (Form L). The mean I.Q. was 68·86 points, S.D. 10·24 points.

Table 16. Frequency Distributions of I.Q.s on Five Intelligence Tests, not Corrected for Differences in S.D. (N=104)

I.Q.	Kohs	Matrices	Binet Voc.	Porteus I.Q.	Cattell*
Median I.Q.	75·36	72·33	71·10	85·69	65·10
Mean I.Q.	75·41	74·55	71·38	82·56	63·78
S.D. of I.Qs.	17·00	12·73	14·89	22·00	14·07
120 +	1	0	2	3	0
110–119	2	1	0	11	0
100–109	5	2	2	4	3
90–99	13	12	5	18	1
80–89	23	16	11	29	4
70–79	20	33	40	13	22
60–69	15	28	23	8	43
50–59	19	10	18	10	15
Less than 50	6	2	3	8	16

Despite differences in the adequacy of the standardization of the tests and their comparative difficulty for institutional defectives, the findings agree in that the average I.Q. (mean or median) of the patients was above 70 points on each of the five tests given to all subjects, and just below 70 points on the full Terman-Merrill test given to half the sample. We concluded that if these results were typical then about half the adults classified as feeble-minded and placed in mental-deficiency institutions were dull rather than defective in intelligence.

(*b*) *Findings obtained by Stickland at Harperbury Hospital*—At about the same time as the Darenth Park study was being made,

* Published figures by CATTELL give the standard deviation of this test as between 20 and 25 points. A "corrected" I.Q. obtained by reducing the standard deviation from 25 to 16 points gives a median I.Q. of 72·08 and a mean of 73·42.

Table 17. *Scores of* 100 *Institutional Patients on Three Tests of Intelligence*

Test	Nature of Score	Mean and SD	Range
1937 Terman-Merrill (Binet)	Mental Age (months)	115 ±32·7	67–249
Progressive Matrices	Raw Score*	22·7 ± 9·7	7– 47
Kohs Blocks	Mental Age (months)	121·5 ±39·9	63–235

Dr. C. A. STICKLAND, at Harperbury Hospital, carried out a somewhat similar investigation of a sample of adult patients in the institution. STICKLAND'S sample consisted of 50 males and 50 females who were considered to be representative of the adult feeble-minded population. The mean ages were: Males 36·8 ±10·6 years; females 34·4 ± 13·0 years, and the patients had been on the average about six years in the institution. The results for three intelligence tests are given below in Table 17.

The mean I.Q.s for the three tests, using the Terman-Merrill conversion table for the Binet and Kohs tests and I.Q. equivalents for the Progressive Matrices are as follows: Terman-Merrill, I.Q. 64; Matrices I.Q. 74, Kohs Blocks I.Q. 67. The defectives in STICKLAND'S sample were on average nearly 15 years older than those in the Darenth study. In neither the Terman-Merrill nor the Kohs Blocks tests are scores for adults corrected for age, and an uncorrected score on these tests certainly underestimates what the performance of adults of 35 years of age and over would be in relation to the general population of their own age. (The Harperbury sample may in addition have been somewhat duller than the Darenth sample, since more of the young brighter patients may have been discharged after being in the institution for a period.)

(c) 100 *male defectives at Darenth Park*—In 1950 a second sample of 100 male adult feeble-minded patients was tested at Darenth Park, using the Progressive Matrices Test, and the Wechsler

---

* For subjects between 20 and 30 years of age a raw score of 23 points is approximately equal to an I.Q. of 74 on a test whose mean is 100; S.D. = 16 points. For an unselected adult population 20–30 years of age the mean raw score on this test = 44 points; S.D. = 10 points.

Bellevue Verbal Scale which became available in England after the first sample had been tested. Both of these tests are suitable for adult defectives—the Matrices because it is an adult intelligence test which has been soundly standardized in this country and which is not too difficult for persons above imbecile level to attempt; the Wechsler test because, although not standardized in England, it has at least been soundly standardized on a representative sample of the United States adult population. The I.Q.s obtained from this second sample had an average of 69·38, and a standard deviation of 10·07 points on the Wechsler verbal scale and on the Progressive Matrices Test a mean score of 24·10 points and a standard deviation of 10·57 points. The mean score of 24 points on the Matrices is equivalent to an I.Q. of about 74 points.

(*d*) *Patients tested at the Manor Hospital*—The most comprehensive study of the intelligence of patients in a single hospital using a well-standardized test is that carried out by Dr. and Mrs. A. D. B. CLARKE, psychologists at the Manor Hospital, Epsom, Surrey (personal communication). Testing 400 consecutive feebleminded adults for certification and recertification purposes with the full Wechsler Bellevue Test they found the mean I.Q. of male patients to be 72 ±12·2 points and the mean I.Q. of female patients to be 74 ±12·6 points. The average age of the sample was about 23 years.

(*e*) *Other investigations*—A number of smaller investigations have been carried out. In the course of the London Survey we tested on the Progressive Matrices Test all feeble-minded adult patients aged between 16 and 30 who were available in the hospitals at the time of our visit. The numbers were small—25 males and 24 females.

The mean raw scores obtained correspond roughly to I.Q.s of 74 and 71 points respectively. These accord with data obtained at Darenth Park and at Harperbury. In other studies we found that 100 male patients tested on Progressive Matrices at the Manor Hospital obtained a mean score equivalent to 74 I.Q. points, and 26 females tested at Darenth obtained a mean score of 71 points.

Discussion

The weight of the evidence, especially that obtained from the use of the Wechsler Bellevue Scale and the Progressive Matrices Test supports the view that the *average* I.Q. of feeble-minded institutional adults is 70 points or more. No less than half the adult patients certified as feeble-minded and placed in institutions in the Greater London Area, and possibly elsewhere, are dull rather than defective in intelligence, however defective they may be "morally". To this finding we attach considerable importance because of its implications for training, education and the resettlement of defectives in the community. We do not consider that the results can be explained merely as practice effects or as artefacts due to "regression toward the mean", but believe that in some cases I.Q.s may have risen as a result of improvement in environmental conditions. They strongly suggest that institutional patients who are graded as feeble-minded need not be kept permanently segregated from the community because of *cognitive* defect. Whether they are "defective" at all depends upon one's definition of mental deficiency, a point which will be taken up in a later chapter. In discussing what should be done with these patients we need to consider very carefully their emotional and social qualities and how far they can be trained to become socially competent. We need too, to discuss how the training of "high-grade" defectives can best equip them to leave an institution and take up a socially useful life in the community in the shortest period of time.

CHAPTER FOUR

PSYCHOMETRIC THEORIES OF STABILITY AND NEUROTIC TENDENCY AMONG DEFECTIVES

THE TASK set for the research to be reported, was to investigate the possibilities of returning defectives to the community. The first investigations were psychometric ones designed to evaluate the performance of feeble-minded adolescent males and to clarify the picture of the relationship between test performances and social and occupational behaviour. The procedure enabled us to make essential contacts in the hospital, and to get to know the people whom we would subsequently attempt to train and employ.

The background of theory which determined the selection of tests, their administration and the results, are described in this chapter and the next.

In the general behaviour of defectives, psychiatrists have frequently detected features similar to those seen in psychosis. "Psychotic" cases are to be found among imbeciles, and patients may, because of psychosis, score on some tests at the performance level of imbeciles. Apart from gross psychosis, behaviour disturbances of a milder variety are known among those with I.Q.s above 50 although still below normal, but there have been very few studies of neurotic behaviour among defectives. An attempt to examine the various aspects of behaviour affected and then to estimate the incidence of disturbance and instability among this group has not been made satisfactorily since the early days of temperament testing. The purpose of this chapter is to formulate questions which are partly answered in the next chapter. The literature is concerned primarily with the relationship between personality and performance, and personality and social adjustment.

Personality and the Performance of Routine Tasks

That the effect of personality could be detected in the performance of routine tasks involving simple movements has long been recognized in so far as the general question of persistence and its

52

relation to academic and work success is concerned. In the form of resistance to monotony, persistence was studied in the decades immediately succeeding the first world war and especially in the 'thirties. The relationship between productivity and persistence was investigated by H. M. VERNON (1921) and by WYATT and LANGDON (1937) for the Industrial Health Research Board. At this time also the speed of operation of neurotics on repetitive tasks was investigated by CULPIN and MAY SMITH (1930). MAY SMITH and ZAKI (1948) subsequently followed up this work. In his original study on the nervous temperament, CULPIN showed that the speed and level of persistence of the obsessional was above that of other workers on repeated monotonous operations. Other neurotics tended to fall below the mean for controls. In a different way, the relationship between lack of co-ordination and lack of emotional integration has been amply demonstrated in the interesting work of LURIA (1932 translation). EYSENCK (1947), in a general discussion of ability and efficiency, gives an extensive review of the literature and concludes that, although it is difficult to assess the significance of the often contradictory findings, there is some indication that a general speed factor underlies performance. On the basis of work by HARRISON (1941) and others, EYSENCK suggests that such a general speed factor is probably unrelated to reaction time, intelligence or fluency. From his own findings with the O'Connor Tweezers test and the speed on the Track Tracer, he is able to show (1947) that these two speed tests have a comparatively high loading on a factor which is designated neuroticism. There would thus appear to be some relationship between this motor speed factor and neurotic tendency.

The existence of a factor of motor speed among defectives has sometimes been noticed in the literature. ABEL (1925) observed that not all mentally-subnormal girls employed on machine work could succeed at the level required of normals. The conclusion drawn by investigators working at this time, such as ABEL, PORTEUS and GODDARD, was that intelligence was related to speed of work on simple manual operations. PORTEUS, quoted by ABEL, reports a correlation of 0·83 between Binet plus Porteus scores and the grading of morons on needlework. In her own experimental work ABEL studied two groups of girls, one of which was composed

of those who were capable of full training in machine operation
and the other of only partial training. She found certain significant
differences both of intelligence and temperament between the two
groups. Those capable of full training were found to have higher
I.Q.s than those capable of only partial training. Important differences were also found with the Downey Will Temperament Test
between the partially trainable group and the fully trainable group.
That these reported differences were not entirely due to differences in intelligence was shown by the comparison of 25 selected
girls from each group matched for intelligence and spatial discrimination. Significant differences were recorded between high
and low performance groups on speed of decision, resistance to
suggestion, volitional perseveration (persistence) and finality of
judgment. No other investigations have been found which show
the existence of a connection between personality differences and
performance on manual tasks among defectives. Unpublished work
of LUBIN (1951), however, showed that discrimination may be
made between psychotics and neurotics by the examination of
scores on simple motor tests.

With defectives the influence of non-cognitive personality traits
on performance is likely to be more difficult to demonstrate because
of the closer association which is known to exist between dexterity
and measured intelligence. Work by ATTENBOROUGH and FARBER
(1934) with Manchester children, first indicated that a higher correlation might be found. A correlation of 0·65 between a battery of
manual dexterity tests and a battery of intelligence tests was reported. Similar correlations of between 0·34 and 0·59 are reported
in another study (O'CONNOR, 1950) between tests of intelligence,
manual dexterity and finger dexterity. However, lower correlations
were obtained in other investigations (O'CONNOR, 1951), between
measures of emotional instability and dexterity (0·193 to 0·292 sig.
at the 5-per-cent and 1-per-cent levels of significance respectively).
Thus, although there is apparently a closer relationship between
the intelligence and dexterity of defectives, the success of an individual at motor performance may not be solely explained in terms
of his I.Q. and a specific ability or specific abilities. Apparently,
even in the case of defectives performance is influenced by emotional stability, although evidence on this point is still limited.

Personality and Social Competence

Many studies reporting follow-up investigations of ex-hospital patients either before, during or after the second world war, whether in England or America, are primarily concerned with the success of the patient in relation to his measured intelligence. The extensive literature on the subject of the defectives' social competence has been summarized by many authors. PORTEUS (1941), LOUTTIT (1947), BICE (1948), and others (TIZARD and O'CONNOR, 1950) have given surveys of the numerous sociological investigations. One of the most recent and exhaustive studies of the defective in the community has been done by REEVES KENNEDY (1948) for Connecticut city. The above listed summaries of previous research and also more recent surveys of which REEVES KENNEDY's work is a representative example, point to a somewhat lower level of adjustment among defectives than among the normal population. Although wages seem to be only slightly related to intelligence as HEGGE (1944) and others have shown, there are some respects in which defectives generally make poorer adjustment than do normals. REEVES KENNEDY's list of significant differences between morons and non-morons matched for age and socio-economic status suggests that more feeble-minded persons are careless and prone to error in their work than others. They are said to learn slowly and to require repeated re-instruction and some show poor judgment and make unreliable decisions. According to this author, they have poor application, waste time and besides being more often late are apt to cause trouble. Corresponding social short-comings are listed, as dependence on relief, police and court records, multiple arrests, divorce and desertion. Such a list suggests a poor work and adjustment record for defectives and gives a picture of the kind of failure which they tend to show. The sample chosen ranged from I.Q. 50 to I.Q. 75 and numbered 256. Such forms of maladjustment have not been related to personality factors in surveys, but some indication of the percentage failure of defectives because of personality maladjustment is given by WEAVER (1946). In a study of 8,000 cases of defectives whom he met as a social worker in the American Red Cross, 56 per cent of the males and 62 per cent of the females made satisfactory adjustment but the remainder had psychiatric and psychosomatic problems or were delinquent. In giving discharge figures WEAVER puts 8 per cent of discharges as due to ineffectiveness, 3 per cent for psychopathic behaviour, 6 per cent for severe anti-social behaviour characterized by emotional immaturity and instability, and 13 per cent on psychiatric and psychosomatic grounds. In the British Army little information seems to have been collected which bears directly on this problem, but ESHER (1941) notes that of 100 cases referred for psychiatric examination, 44 per cent had been in the army more than six months before breakdown.

Investigations which bear directly on the incidence of mental disturbance in defectives will be examined in the next section. It remains to note here that few studies have been made on defectives which directly relate qualities or personality to occupational adequacy. However, it is widely believed by hospital staff members that the initial adjustment difficulties of defectives seriously affect their social competence and job success. Of the studies made, that of FOULDS (1945) deserves note. He showed that defectives who react differently to frustration tend to have different work attitudes. Using ROSENZWEIG'S (1938) classification, he found that extra-punitive or aggressive boys tended not to stay long on jobs, whereas intro-punitives were more amenable. This research appears to be the only work applying these frustration concepts to defectives and their employment success.

The Relationship between Instability or Neurosis and Employment Success

Among large-scale studies of neurotics, poor work records have frequently been recognized as a correlate of the presence of neurotic symptoms. CULPIN and MAY SMITH (1930) state that there is apparently "a direct relationship between efficiency and the absence of nervous symptoms". The work of WEAVER (1946) and DEWAN (1948) with defectives in the Canadian army, and EYSENCK (1947) with a non-defective army sample support the view implicit in such surveys as that of RUSSELL FRASER (1947) with factory workers, that neurosis shows itself either in inefficiency or complete breakdown. HUNT and COFER (1944) express in general terms the same conclusion. Symptoms, such as intolerance of effort, poor muscular tone and frequent unemployment have been associated with neurosis by EYSENCK (1947), while MAXWELL JONES (1948) in an exhaustive study of stress in neurotics reports effort intolerance and physical inferiority as characteristic of the patients examined. A further study of the association between neurosis and work failure has been carried out by RUSSELL DAVIS (1948 and 1949). His work indicates the kind of errors which occur under stress and suggests that these are associated with diagnosed neurosis. Although work failure in workers of average intelligence may not often occur in such high percentages as those reported by RUSSELL FRASER (1947) as due to disabling neurosis, one would expect neurosis to handicap performance. When mental defect is present in association with neurosis or similar mental disorder, an even higher correlation with occupational work failure might be expected. Whether either proposition is true will be discussed later.

The kind of failure which is mentioned by REEVES KENNEDY (1948), and the account of over-reaction and under-reaction which is discussed by RUSSELL DAVIS (1948, 1949), present two aspects of work failure in subjects of widely differing abilities. There is sufficient similarity in the descriptions offered to suggest that the causes for failure may not be unrelated. The most noticeable similarity is in the lack of capacity for sustained attention and persistence manifested in learning and performance.

Other investigations show that emotional instability or neuroticism is related to lack of persistence on the job, accident proneness and susceptibility to monotony.

THORNTON, in one of the first adequate studies of persistence (1939) concluded that only a limited number of workers had the persistence required for monotonous repetitive work. The same observation was earlier made by WYATT, FROST and STOCK (1934) as the result of workshop investigations. KREMER (1942) reports such an association with persistence and emotional instability to the extent of $r = 0.299$ ($N = 156$). The reliability of the battery used in this investigation was 0.85. RYANS (1938) reports similar but slightly higher correlations of 0.38 and 0.48. KREMER also reports that a significant negative correlation was found between persistence and suggestibility. In conformity with KREMER's findings are those of THOMPSON (1929), that tendency to fatigue and boredom

E

is related to emotional instability. Such results would also be accepted as confirming those of THORNTON in so far as lack of persistence is believed to be related to emotional instability.

The literature on proneness to injury has been summarized by GHISELLI and BROWN (1948). Results appear to be contradictory but evidence collected so far both in England and America since the pioneer work of GREENWOOD and WOODS (1919) and H. M. VERNON (1921), suggest that the majority of accidents due to human error are caused by a comparatively small proportion of workers. Greenwood and Woods believed that some workers are innately more clumsy than others, Vernon lays stress on the worker's psychological attitude and Ghiselli and Brown summing up previous research, affirm that the two major causes of accidents are poor physical health and mental stress. These two causes are more important than age, fatigue or lack of familiarity with the job. RUSSELL DAVIS in recent work (1949) emphasizes the importance of mental stress and regards the lack of responsiveness to relevant stimuli which he finds to be associated with accidents, as characteristically neurotic.

The findings reported in this section together with the factor analytic findings of EYSENCK (1947) suggest that a general factor of persistence whilst apparently related to work efficiency, is also found to be associated with freedom from neurosis. In a similar way susceptibility to monotony and accident proneness, while obviously factors which affect industrial efficiency, have been shown to be correlated with neurotic symptoms.

The Personality of High-grade Defectives

From the literature surveyed in the previous pages it can be inferred that a connection exists between neurotic personality and work failure. The extent to which defectives fail in jobs in the community, or the extent of their success on unskilled work in comparison with normal workers, has been widely investigated. Estimates of percentage successes vary from 50 per cent (HOLT, 1943) to over 80 per cent, e.g. HEGGE (1944) and KENNEDY (1948). Many findings lie between these two extremes such as those of KINDER, CHASE and BUCK (1941), BIJOU, AINSWORTH and STOCKEY (1943), THOMAS (1943), MUENCH (1944), COAKLEY (1945) and

McKEON (1946). The majority of investigations which were conducted under a variety of conditions suggest that a percentage
success between 60 per cent and 80 per cent is characteristic.* A
slightly lower figure is found for the employment of defectives in
the army under conditions of war-time stress.

How far success and failure at work is due to personality difficulties has not been investigated so thoroughly, despite the considerable research which has centred round the social and psychological life of the high-grade hospital population. The possible
range of defective personality is sometimes assumed to be narrow,
but few systematic or objective studies have been made. One of
the earliest pronouncements on the personality of the feeble-
minded was made by DOLL (1932). Doll offered as his opinion, the
view that the defective personality showed a wide range of variation, but variations, while no less than those to be found among
normals, were often more transitory. TREDGOLD (1908; edition of
1947) gives a description of high-grade defective children which
stresses their comparative passivity and lack of vitality. That
patterns of personality disorder do not differ greatly from those
found among the more intelligent, however, may be inferred from
his statement that hysteria and anxiety neurosis can be found in
defectives and that neuroses are in fact more common among
defectives than among normals. TREDGOLD believes that at adolescence it is often difficult to distinguish high-grade mental defect
from psychoneurosis and dementia. The differentiation of the
defective personality has been little attempted apart from clinical
observations and studies of "pseudo-feeble-mindedness". PENROSE
for example (1938) notes that hysteria, obsessions and psychopathic personality and depression frequently occur among
defectives.

FOULDS (1944, 1945) has shown how a further basic differentiation of defective personality can be made. He applied the Rosenzweig Triadic hypothesis, i.e. that there are three types of reaction
to frustration, to groups of defectives in an agricultural hostel and
was able to predict how they would behave at work. A series of

---

* BINET (1914) makes a similar note: "73 per cent of defectives have been
made—or have become—more or less useful."

projective sketches is shown to patients, who are asked to supply conversations for the people depicted in the sketches. Their reactions show whether they tend to blame themselves or others for frustrating events or whether they take a "can't be helped" or impunitive attitude. A similar study of frustration and reaction to frustration is reported in the following year. FOULDS suggests that the parent-child relationship determines how both mental defectives and normal children will respond in frustrating situations. He believes that large numbers of high-grade defectives living in hospitals are intro-punitive (personal communication 1948). FOULDS disputes the view of ROSENZWEIG that intro-punitiveness results from long residence in hospitals, on the grounds that extra-punitive defectives do not become less so.

FALLS and BLAKE (1948) found intro-punitiveness to be slightly correlated with dominance and hypomania and inversely with scholastic aptitude. The relative incidence of intro-punitive, extra-punitive and impunitive reactions among defectives has not been investigated apart from the work of FOULDS and ROSENZWEIG. SARASON (1949) does not mention their work in what is probably the most detailed and recent overall survey of previous and current work on the psychology of mental deficiency.

That the categories of mental disorder and mental deficiency are frequently confused and are probably interrelated is widely accepted. TREDGOLD (1947), PENROSE (1938), SARASON (1949), SLOAN (1947) and JOLLES (1947) among many others have drawn attention to this fact in different ways. The work of RANK (1949) and KANNER (1943) has focused attention on similar problems in psychiatry. In other studies (O'CONNOR and YONGE, 1955; YONGE and O'CONNOR, 1954) we have also shown a connection between treatment and I.Q. gain. WALLIN (1949) has summarized the evidence and concludes that insufficient knowledge makes a decision on this topic premature. He notices the divergent views of NEUER (1947) and KALLMAN and co-workers (1941) on the topic of the association between schizophrenia and defect. KALLMAN maintains that psychosis is found more frequently among those of normal and superior intelligence than among the defectives. NEUER on the other hand states that mental deficiency is the result of a major or minor psychosis in childhood. Many of the feeble-minded, says WALLIN, are subject to psychotic or psychoneurotic episodes which although transitory may last several days. The existence of such states which are essentially faulty behaviour patterns adopted by the defective to solve his adjustment problems may be taken for signs of genuine psychosis, or for permanent psychopathy. The particular pattern adopted, believes WALLIN, will depend on three variables, the situation, the personality of the defective and his intelligence. The range of such behaviour is wide, including "periods of excitement, emotional outbursts, maniacal attacks, agitated or passive depression, anxiety, apathy, indifference, resistance, obstinacy, irritability, seclusiveness, withdrawal from social contacts, unprovoked laughter or crying, hysterical pains or paralyses, childish behaviour, night terrors, specific phobias, confusion, delusions, hallucinations, automatisms (such as meaningless repetition of words or actions), quaint mannerisms, and the like."

Despite this interesting and comprehensive description the nature of the association between mental disorder and defect has not been decided. Divergent views presented by WALLIN range from statements that the occasional occurrences of the two is coincidental, to statements that both conditions result from the same genotype.

Referring to the customary division of defectives into unstable, restless, psychopathic, hyperkinetic or labile as opposed to the slow, asthenic, and placid types, WALLIN suggests that most defectives fall between these two groups and occasionally manifest one set of symptoms and sometimes the other, whereas a good number are neither phlegmatic nor labile but neutral or indifferent. He states that the category of psychopathy has been used in so many different contexts that its rejection is recommended.

However the question of psychopathy is decided, it is obvious that defectives differ greatly among themselves in their personalities. In this respect they resemble normal people.

Whether in fact the complete range of normal personality can be found in the defective may not be a meaningful question. Theoretically, the degree of differentiation, and correspondingly the degree of integration, possible to the intelligent, well-educated normal adult would be impossible for even the high-grade defective.

LURIA (1932) in his analysis of emotion, conflict and will, indicates a possible difference between neurotics of average intelligence and defectives with associated mental disorder. His experiments were carried out with JUNG's Word Association techniques plus this additional measure. A word was presented to the subject and he was asked to respond with the first word which occurred to him in the usual way. At the same time as he gave the response he was to press down with one hand on a stirrup in which his right hand was fastened. The left hand, in a similar stirrup, was to be kept quite still. A stimulus which was emotionally neutral might lead to a quick word response and a small controlled pressure of the right hand. An emotionally disturbing stimulus word, on the other hand, might result in a delay in word response accompanied by a jerky pressure of both hands. In other words, motor response ceases to be precise and directed, and becomes instead more general and less co-ordinated.

His suggestion is that precision of motor response is determined not only by the comparative lability of the nervous system but in addition by the degree of cortical control which freedom from conflict may permit. Stimuli in children tend to lead to a response of the whole organism. In adults the response will be more specific and will depend on two factors according to this theory. The first is the degree to which overall response has become conditioned, and the second is the amount of direct conflict in the inhibiting (cortical) control mechanism. An example of the first would be the confusion and tendency to overt, undifferentiated motor response, because of poverty of the subject's vocabulary. An example of the second is the kind of conflict situation which, LURIA claims, is characteristic of the responses of those to whom special stimuli have unusual affective content. Such stimuli evoke a spreading over of emotional response into the motor area thus interfering with the more specific learned response. The importance of the study of movement in relation to defect and its mental disorders is seen in the simple experimental work which LURIA attempted with defectives (approximate I.Q. 60). It is suggested in this work that it might be possible to distinguish between a neurotic type of motor reaction and a defective reaction. The defective response is characterized by an irradiation of motor response into inappropriate general motor movements. With the neurotic such movement responses occur in only few instances whereas for the most part responses are precise and relevant involving a minimum of muscles. Whether reactions of a neurotic type can be found in a defective otherwise well integrated, is so far a matter for conjecture. The work of LURIA has not been followed up with defectives but studies have been made of their manual dexterity, hand-eye co-ordination, and general locomotor co-ordination. Most of this information has been related to general intelligence. The work begun by LURIA needs considerable further research but is mentioned here because of the experimental findings to be presented later which show a connection between emotional instability among defectives and their overall dexterity and speed of response.

Other aspects of the personality of defectives which have been occasionally referred to are persistence, suggestibility and power of attention. The literature on these subjects is slight and will be dealt with in examining experimental results. In brief, it is generally held that defectives are more suggestible than the normally intelligent, and likely to be less persistent. They are also supposed to be incapable of sustained attention. TREDGOLD (1947) suggests that lack of powers of concentration in the defective are characteristic of the condition and recommends the use of BOURDON'S cancellation test to measure this lack of attention. The test is one which consists of cancelling one particular letter from a page of randomly distributed letters. Such tests have been used for 40 years as measures of persistence.

Apart from the recent work of EYSENCK (1943), EYSENCK and FURNEAUX (1945), and EYSENCK and REES (1945) on suggestibility and work referred to by EYSENCK (1950), there have been few studies of suggestibility. The most important for our purposes is that of BRADY (1948) showing that there is no unusual primary suggestibility among epileptics or defectives. Subsequent work by O'CONNOR (1951) confirms this finding.

Apart from the special discussion of the incidence of emotional instability in the next section, it can be said of the investigations referred to here that the picture which they give of the defective personality is surprisingly varied. Such descriptions range from that of TREDGOLD which describes the typical defective child as inert and lacking in vitality, to the long list of descriptive adjectives used in Wallin's account of possible changes of mood in the defective. It is characteristic of the uncertainty which prevails that it should be necessary for Wallin to admit that most defectives are neither phlegmatic nor labile, and that SARASON (1949), after a long discussion of the value of projective tests with defectives concludes that the study of the defective personality is only just beginning.

The Incidence of Mental Disturbance among High-grade Defectives

The incidence of emotional instability and neurosis or mental disorder among defectives has been incidentally referred to by many authors. PENROSE (1938) gives figures of the incidence of mild and acute psychopathy in the 1,280 cases studied at the Royal Eastern Counties Institution. He found 72 severely psychopathic or psychotic and 132 mildly psychopathic or neurotic. The percentage of neurotic patients was therefore just over 10 per cent, and 16 per cent in all could be graded as either psychotic or neurotic.

The figure of 10 per cent neurotics in a hospital population compares with objective test findings which will be given below but notice should be taken of a wide survey conducted in the Canadian army by DEWAN (1948). Psychiatrists succeeding each other for duty found an average of 47·7 per cent of those of low or defective intelligence to be emotionally unstable. Such a large number of cases graded unstable obviously indicates different diagnostic methods from those used in the English studies. Some 40 psychiatrists were involved, and psychiatric diagnosis of instability was compared with intelligence scores on the Canadian army M. Test. Figures of instability decreased progressively as intelligence increased.

It was also observed that a tendency to instability occurred at the other end of the intelligence scale, despite the general apparent correlation between intelligence and freedom from emotional instability. The explanation given for the two phenomena was the further hypothesis that the instability of an individual increases as he is cut off from his environment or the common activities of his fellows. Poor and very superior intelligence are regarded as creating such participation barriers.

Most investigators familiar with mental defect have concurred in supposing that the incidence of instability is higher here than among those of normal intelligence. DUNCAN (1936), WEAVER (1946), NEUER (1947), KINGSLEY and HYDE (1945) in America, and VERNON (1937) and EYSENCK (1947) have discussed this matter. There is general agreement that there is a low negative correlation between intelligence and susceptibility to neurosis. It is sometimes supposed that the correlation is largely due to the incidence of instability at the extremes of the scale of intelligence, and differential social stress has been offered as an explanation of why people of low intelligence tend to break down under some conditions of stress, while people of high intelligence tend to break down under others (EYSENCK, 1947).

Surveys of the non-defective population sometimes show a lower incidence of neurosis than was reported by DEWAN, although not much lower than Penrose's figures. For example, WALLIN (1949) found about 6·7 per cent to be neurotic or nervous from 2,774 school children in his St. Louis clinic. RUSSELL FRASER (1947) found 10 per cent disabling neurosis and 20 per cent mild neurosis among war-time factory workers living under war-time stress. Although these figures are somewhat divergent and probably reflect different standards of classification and diagnosis as well as differences in the ages and degrees of stress of the samples considered, there appears to be general agreement that neurosis of a more or less disabling kind will be found in about 10 per cent to 20 per cent of the population. MENNINGER (1948) quoted figures of the number of service inductees rejected for neurotic disorders. Calculation shows the number to represent 12·3 per cent of all men examined. Subsequently a further 2·8 per cent were rejected for the same reason. The expectancy of mental treatment at some time during their lives for people living in New York State is 8·3 per cent according to TIETZE (1943). There is no doubt from these figures that DEWAN's findings represent an unusually high figure for the incidence of mental breakdown among mental defectives. It is more especially obvious as the incidence which he gives for those of normal intelligence under the same conditions, 26·7 per cent, more nearly corresponds with findings reported by RUSSELL FRASER. It would seem likely therefore that the incidence of emotional disturbance among the defective is higher than among the normal population, but not so high as DEWAN suggests. DUNCAN (1936), and HENDERSON and GILLESPIE (1930), also support this point of view as do WEAVER, NEUER, KINGSLEY and HYDE and DEWAN, whilst POLLOCK (1944) states "the general incidence of mental illness is higher among subnormal persons than among the general population and our data indicates that the rate of mental disease declines as the degree of intelligence advances".

It may be expected, therefore, that a higher figure for instability and emotional disturbance will be found in any defective population than for a normal population, and that the figure is likely to be unusually high in hospitals where patients are often sent because disturbed, or "psychopathic", rather than because they are cognitively defective.

The effect that this tendency to emotional disturbance is likely to have on the work adjustment of the defective has been indicated. Its full implications will be further discussed below.

The Comparative Study of Psychometric Theories of Neuroticism

Although only the more general nature of psychometric theories of neurosis has been outlined here, enough has been said to indicate that these theories are primarily concerned with constitutional predisposition. In the next chapter where neurotic breakdown and work success are discussed, the list of variables includes such tests as intolerance of effort, pulse rate, psycho-galvanometer, speed of movement, body build and similar measures which are primarily selected and recommended because of their supposed relative invariability from day to day for one person. A presupposition of the approach described here is the invariability of certain aspects of human structure and the relevance of this psychological structure to certain qualities of behaviour. The object of the psychometrician concerned with isolating personality determinants of neurosis is to define by psychometric analysis a small group of "factors" which may be held to account for the complex of symptoms known as neurosis. EYSENCK (1953) formulates a logic for the use of factor analysis in determining the constitutional elements which contribute to neurotic breakdown. Such procedures may be regarded as purely formal techniques of classification as BURT might suggest, or as having an underlying material and causal nexus which EYSENCK would say is the case.

The theory underlying factor analysis is not debated here, as the main work was carried out with multiple regression techniques. This technique allows for the computation of the relationship between each of a series of tests or variables and a criterion variable such as work success or emotional instability. The relationships can be assessed independently for each variable and the criterion and these independent relationships added to show the relationship of all measures as a whole to the criterion measure. The tests are sometimes said to predict the criterion in so far as knowing a score of any individual on a set of tests and the relationship between these tests and the criterion, the individual's score on the criterion can be predicted, or estimated in advance. Thus theoretically his work success, for example, or his chance of succeeding at work could be estimated before he had been given a trial on a job.

Although prediction is regarded correctly as one of the marks of the ability to control phenomena, it can exist where there is as yet no possibility of such control. The weather is a case in point. We may not even understand the causes of the events which we can predict with some accuracy, because what we predict as a unitary phenomenon may conceal a multiplicity of sources of variation in the quantity or quality of that phenomenon. Thus the refinement of a factor "g" is not a guarantee that lack of intelligence in one person will be due to the same causes as those which account for intellectual deficit in another.

Such theoretical uncertainty suggests caution in interpreting results which may sometimes appear relatively clear and decisive. However, in this field a greater caution is demanded because of the complexity of the factors involved and the fact that few reliable measures are available to enable us to determine future behaviour with accuracy. To counsel the rejection of a patient for some trial job on the basis of even a set of well standardized scores, means to prevent him from taking an opportunity which, because of some consideration as yet not measured, may lead him to success and rehabilitation. Under such circumstances, the selection or rejection of an individual on psychometric grounds may be indefensible because of the margin of error.

It would seem better to give the patient the benefit of the doubt even if this leads to a new failure. Considerations of this sort are taken into account in interpreting the results to be presented in the succeeding chapters. Thus the findings of the next chapter are regarded as of theoretical interest, suggesting lines of further research, but data available do not provide a basis for a practical policy of selection.

CHAPTER FIVE

THE PREDICTION OF OCCUPATIONAL SUCCESS: TWO INVESTIGATIONS

The Logic of Prediction

THE HYPOTHESIS that emotional instability or neurosis and work capacity are related has been put forward frequently. As described in the previous chapter, there can be no doubt that in certain instances neurosis is disabling. However, it is not in every instance that neurosis becomes a handicap for work, as the work of CULPIN and MAY SMITH (1930) and more recently the valuable studies of MARKOWE and BARBER (1953) and HERON (1955) have shown with factory workers. As MARKOWE and BARBER say (1953) "The more severe the neurotic disability of men who left work, the longer they stayed before leaving." But with reservations involving both the nature of employment and conditions of the labour market it is true to say that of 21 men and 52 women who left their employment during one study (1953) about 60 per cent were judged to be neurotic. The percentage is significantly higher than the percentage leaving from among the group who were not judged to be neurotic. This is the general finding of other studies. The same finding will be shown to hold with our own results with defectives of intelligence level 50 to 120 points with a mean of 70 points. However, the nature of prediction is such that as with the papers referred to, results obtained with one study are not always confirmed under different circumstances.

Part of the reason for this sort of variability is the great variety of circumstances which lie outside the field of psychological and certainly of psychometric study. Thus a prediction study cannot hope to compensate for administrative changes which may be introduced during a follow-up period, modifying the tolerance of a neurotic group for a certain kind of job. Another source of error is the unreliability of the test measures used. When studies were originally carried out on tests of various kinds held to offer an operational definition of neurosis, their reliability was usually measured over limited periods of time such as one or two days, a week or sometimes a month. In many cases reliabilities were obtained by split half techniques. In relation to individual performance, reliabilities obtained in this way show that the subjects tested are likely to behave in the same way over short periods. However even at this level reliabilities are frequently too low to guarantee any exact replication of say a closely similar rank order of results on one test by the same group of people. When the reliabilities are tested over a period of about 6 months or one year they tend to be lower than in more recent re-tests and are in fact so low that the probability of replication is greatly reduced.

The hazards of prediction depending on such considerations have been discussed at length in relation to the selection of school children by DEARBORN and ROTHNEY (1941), and in air force selection by R. L. THORNDIKE (1949). THORNDIKE gives an interesting table which is reproduced here as an indication of the kind of findings which selection for a task by one group of tests is likely to give rise to. The group was screened for a flying training school on the basis of the aptitude tests.

Table 18. *Effectiveness of Selection by Aptitude Test*

(Cost of selection programme, in terms of potential successes rejected, compared with utility, in terms of potential failures rejected for different qualifying standards. Sample of 1000 cases)

Minimum Aptitude Test Score to Qualify	Cost: per cent Successes Rejected	Utility: per cent Failures Rejected
85	99·4	100·0
80	96·3	100·0
75	86·2	99·0
70	70·8	93·9
65	55·7	81·5
60	22·6	62·8
55	5·6	40·3
50	·3	24·1
45	·0	16·0
40	·0	3·7
35	·0	·8
None	·0	·0

The column on the left of Table 18 represents a number of cut-off scores which might be chosen. It will be seen that in this case each improvement is achieved at a certain cost.

It is in relation to this kind of cost that prediction studies in psychometry must be judged. The findings are generally by no means precise enough for efficient vocational guidance as opposed to personnel selection even though they may at one particular time appear to be better than chance. Uncontrolled variables may within a relatively short time radically complicate the picture. Studies such as those of SKEELS and HARMS (1948), HONZIK, MACFARLANE and ALLEN (1948), in the field of education, CLARKE and CLARKE (1953) in the field of intelligence measurement and WOODROW (1939) and COX (1934) on the subject of changes in manual performance, present the other side of the picture, namely the great likelihood of change in one individual. Thus the relationships which are revealed by psychometric studies or any studies which are based on the presupposition of the continuance of a current state of affairs, may in some cases be of transitory significance. Studies with mental defectives, it might be thought, would escape this stricture because of the "permanent" nature of their defect, but even in this case considerable variation occurs.

It is necessary to say all this in advance in order to avoid the conclusion which is sometimes drawn on the basis of comparatively high multiple correlations between a set of variables and a criterion, that the connection of tests and events is in fact such that the relationship can be regarded as a scientific law. The overall conclusions presented in the two studies to be reported in this chapter are impressive by general standards of work in this field and in psychometrics related to the study of personality, and for this reason it is doubly necessary to be cautious. More will be said on this issue when the two investigations have been described.

The general conclusions presented and justified by the evidence collected may be stated as follows: Defectives of feeble-minded grade, that is of measured intelligence level above about 50 points are handicapped in the performance of simple manual work and in job holding primarily by emotional and consequent social handicaps rather than for reasons of lack of intelligence or skill. Despite variations in results between identical tests in the two separate studies this conclusion can still be held.

The Two Investigations

In 1949–50 and 1950–51, two investigations were carried out with feeble-minded male hospital patients who had no gross physical handicaps. Both investigations were carried out with about the same number of patients, 104 in the first case and 100 in the second. Both made use of the same psychometric techniques which are described in the next section and both used tests of a similar nature.

The two investigations overlapped in so far as some subjects were asked to do both batteries of tests and others did only the first or the second. In addition, some tests were common to both batteries. Thus, in cases where individuals had done the tests before, their scores were not included because these might not represent their unpractised performance. However, the same circumstance also permitted the reliability of the tests to be measured. Thus, a first score and second score for a number of patients could be compared for similarities to see whether they were consistent from one time to the next.

The purpose of both studies was to predict neurotic tendency and work success and to show the relationship between them. The main difference between these otherwise cross-checking studies was that in one the criterion of work success was based on estimates, as the patients had not yet been tried, and in the other, later study, on actual work records for those who had been tried at work. The statistics and tests used in the two studies are described in the following pages. On the basis of the results, the relationship of each test to the two criteria could be estimated and the relationship between neurotic tendency and occupational adaptation assessed.

Statistics Used in the Investigations

A little more will be said here on the question of the statistical techniques employed and on the detailed material which justified the inclusion of particular tests.

The technique considered most appropriate was the technique of multiple regression, which is generally believed to give the maximum prediction and to select the variables with the greatest significant correlation with the criterion predicted. A special method of carrying out this regression was employed in this case, the Square Root Method developed by LUBIN and SUMMERFIELD (1951). The full mathematical justification for this method is given by the authors, but a brief account of its purpose and value is given below.* Nothing further need be said of the method of selection of variables except to add that some check on the accuracy of the findings was carried out by applying a separate technique, that of factor analysis.

The Criteria

Criteria to be predicted were chosen on the basis of psychiatric diagnosis or behaviour record in the case of the criterion of neurotic tendency, and on the basis of assessment on actual success at work in the case of the criterion of employment success. In the first study a simple criterion rating was given in each case after a clinical interview by one of the psychiatrists who knew the subjects.† His rating was compared with independent ratings of the patients on the same scale by the two investigators. The median inter-rater reliability was 0·50. The agreement of the raters was improved by discussion and in all cases the complete agreement of

---

* "The logic of the method of analysis set out below takes account of the possible presence of suppressor variables within the battery. It aims to eliminate the variables which may appear to have a significant correlation with the criterion, but which do not add significantly to the multiple correlation over and above the predicted variance due to a smaller number of effective variables.

"The zero order intercorrelation matrix of the variables and the criterion is analysed into a triangular matrix, the diagonal factor matrix. The communality of the criterion where the criterion is not one of the diagonal factors is the squared multiple correlation of the criterion with the battery. Whether this multiple correlation is greater than zero can then be tested by an analysis of variance. If it is not significant then no multiple regression equation is justified. If, however, the multiple correlation is significantly different from zero, the next step in the procedure is to calculate the multiple correlations successively for each variable, giving the highest contribution to the variance of the criterion. The first variable chosen will therefore be the one with highest zero order validity. The next to be chosen is indicated by the correlation of all independent variables with the criterion when the effect of the first variable is held constant for each independent variable. The increase in predicted variance is analysed for significance for each successive variable and the procedure ceases at the point where an added variable contributes no further significant predicted variance."

† This Psychiatric assessment was made by Dr. J. M. CRAWFORD, at that time Deputy Physician Superintendent of Darenth Park.

F

all three raters was required before a rating was accepted. The rating divided all 104 defectives into four groups on the basis of stability of social behaviour. The four groups were:

		N
0.	Very stable and mature	44
1.	Stable but immature	14
2.	Rather unstable	32
3.	Markedly unstable	14

The more stable were marked by maturity of judgment and an easy social attitude. They showed restraint and an adult approach to test and interview situations. The second group were similar but showed signs of social immaturity, shyness and uncertainty. The rather unstable group was noticeably more anxious and pre-occupied. They frequently asked questions about themselves and their future and displayed clear signs of confusion concerning the purpose of the tests and were vaguely suspicious of the tester's intentions. The markedly unstable were the most difficult to inter-view and found difficulty in concentrating on the tests or the interviewer's questions. Their own questions were mostly con-cerned with themselves and in some cases they showed marked aggressiveness and in others very marked anxiety.

In the second study the criterion was based on what appeared to be a more objective measure of disturbance, namely the number of events in the hospital books of a kind believed to warrant dis-ciplinary procedure. An analysis of the hospital records concerning the behaviour of each subject was made. This was quantified and included as a measure in the battery. The essential assumption of this scale is that behaviour of a socially deviant kind will be deter-mined by emotional instability.

Each measure was based on records which are quite reliable, being maintained as a matter of routine within the hospital. Items included in the scale are escapes attempted, detentions awarded, enuresis recorded, reported sick, and awarded parole. The award of parole is only given in cases of good behaviour and this score was therefore subtracted from the others. Scores over a fixed period were assessed for each item and a sum score derived. As some boys were found to have a negative score because they had not attempted to escape, were not detained, showed no enuresis or malingering and had been awarded parole, a constant of 10 was added to each sum score. The resulting measure was regarded as a measure of Social Stability or Unstable Behaviour. A high score indicates a boy with a long record of behaviour difficulties.

This measure is regarded as more objective and valid than the clinical rating of instability previously used.*

A supplementary measure of unstable behaviour was given in the second study as in the first but was included as a predicting variable rather than as a criterion. A psychiatrist† was requested to rate all subjects on a four-point scale of neurosis. This scale presented some difficulties to the psychiatrist who shared the views of DOLL (1932) that clearly defined neurotic symptoms in defectives are seldom apparent. After interviewing each defective in the investigation, however, he divided them into four groups:

> Not neurotic
> Mildly neurotic; some signs of anxiety not usually leading to behaviour disorders
> Moderately neurotic; neurotic symptoms usually accompanied by behaviour disorders
> Severely neurotic; behaviour disorders due to neurotic symptoms

The criteria of work success used in both investigations were very similar but experience dictated the use of slightly modified categories in the second investigation. They are both given for comparison in Tables 19 and 20. The figures given under the heading "*N*" represent the number of cases in each category. There is no continuous principle of classification in the scales because part refers to success inside the hospital and part to success outside. However, this situation although involving a logical hiatus, represents the best available criterion.

The Selection of Predicting Variables

Tables 21 and 22 show the inter-correlation of the variable used

---

* See appendix.
† This psychiatric scale was applied by Dr. G. M. TUCKER of Darenth Park.

Table 19. *Rating Scale of Work Success—I*

	Rating Scale	N
Conspicuous all-round success on daily licence	7	6
Settled down well in first job on daily licence	6	13
Satisfactory on daily licence after not more than two replacements	5	17
Settled on daily licence after several trials	4	30
Failed consistently on daily licence	3	16
Can work in institution conditions, but in the judgment of the chief male nurse and social worker is unlikely to be considered for licence	2	14
Was unsuccessful in institution workshop	1	8
		104

Table 20. *Rating Scale of Work Success—II*

(8) Suitable for resident licence.

(7) Very successful but not yet quite suitable for resident licence.

(6) Holds his job not quite up to physical and mental standard of (8) and (7). May be suitable for resident licence in the future.

(5) Has difficulty in holding his job because of behaviour difficulties. May improve and may subsequently be suitable for resident licence.

(4) Unlikely to go on resident licence at any time because of poor physical and mental capacity.

(3) Has been unsuccessful on daily licence but may be given another trial. No question of these patients going on resident licence while behaviour difficulties continue.

(2) Unsuccessful on daily licence on many occasions, needs a long period of training before re-trial on daily licence.

(1) Custodial cases. Under present circumstances can be regarded as having no prospects of daily licence.

to predict the two criteria in the two studies. Not all the tests were used to predict the criteria in the second study because the sample overlapped to some extent, and for some patients this would therefore have been their second experience of the test, whereas it would have been only the first for others. To avoid possible contamination of the results by practice and other effects, only tests not used before were used in prediction in the second study. Thus Table 23 contains intercorrelations of tests which were not used in

Table 21. *Zero Order Correlation Matrix. Cognitive, Motor, and Personality Test Battery (First Investigation) June 1950*

$N = 104$

Significance level of Zero Order Correlation: 5% = ·193, 1% = ·252

Variable	No.	1	2	3	4	5	6	7	8	9	10	11	12	13	14	C	Reliability Ratios
Anx.-Aggr. Rating	1	—															Median Intra-Rater Consistency ·44
Manual Dext. (U.S.E.S. M & N)	2	27	—														
Finger Dext. (U.S.E.S. O & P)	3	31	66	—													·96 retest, 15 months (O'CONNOR, 1951)
Matrices (1938)	4	39	35	39	—												·94 retest (HEATH, 1943); ·78 retest, 15 months (O'CONNOR, 1951)
Rail Walking Test	5	29	45	44	20	—											·73 retest, 15 months (O'CONNOR, 1951)
Leg Persistence Test	6	−05	06	04	05	02	—										
Dynamom. Persistence Test	7	−07	08	01	−03	−04	22	—									·80 retest, one week (FESSARD, 1936); ·32, 15 months (O'Connor, 1951)
Body Sway Test	8	−24	−20	−19	−24	−09	−14	00	—								·91 retest, one week (EYSENCK & FURNEAUX, 1945); ·84 retest, one month (EYSENCK, 1947) ·07 retest, 15 months (O'CONNOR, 1951)
Four Pt. Instability Rating	9	−35	−24	−29	−23	−30	−01	21	32	—							Median Intra-rater consistency ·50
Index of Flexibility	10	−05	−20	−24	−06	−13	−03	−03	01	10	—						
Speed on Track Tracer	11	−20	−40	−37	−32	−22	05	06	24	20	06	—					·95 Split half (GOULD, 1939); ·29 Median retest (Analysis of GOULD'S data)
Goal Discrepancy	12	−15	−12	−08	−22	−03	−18	15	31	13	−07	36	—				·72 retest (FRANK, 1935)
Judgment Discrepancy	13	−14	−21	−17	−34	−10	−14	05	13	12	−16	42	75	—			
Index of Responsiveness	14	09	−13	−08	06	−02	06	00	−22	02	63	06	−18	−20	—		
Employability Criterion	C	35	45	39	34	44	00	−04	−33	−47	05	−28	−09	−14	11	—	·66 retest, 15 months (O'CONNOR, 1951)

the multiple regression study. Where reliabilities are available they have been quoted.

In the first investigation tests fell into six categories:

> Intelligence tests
> Dexterity and co-ordination tests
> Complex personality measures
> Measures of reaction to achievement
> Persistence tests
> Tests of suggestibility

In the second investigation tests could be divided into the same groups with the exception that the Measures of Achievement Reaction (Goal Discrepancy, etc.) were not included and other physiological measures were put into the battery. The categories were therefore:

Description and Numbers of Variables (See Table 22)

Intelligence tests	25	26	27		
Dexterity and co-ordination tests	10	11	12	13	
Complex personality measures	22	23	24	28	29
Measures of effort tolerance	14	15	16	17	18
Measures of response to stress	3	4	5		
Measures of body build	2				
Persistence tests	19	20	21		
Tests of suggestibility	8	9			
Speed-choice tests	6	7			
Age	1				

Number 30 is of course the criterion of work success.

The groups which are common to both batteries and in fact each of the categories in both batteries may be classified as measures which show the behaviour of subjects in intellectual tasks, motor tasks, or in tasks in the performance of which personality factors may play a predominant part in determining ultimate level of achievement. To justify the exclusion or inclusion of any particular group of tests would require rather more space than can be allotted to this problem at this time. In all cases previous workers in the field of personality theory have found justification for suggesting

Reliability Ratios

·67 retest, 15 months (O'CONNOR, 1951)

·78 retest, 15 months (O'CONNOR, 1951)

·79 retest (CURETON, 1945)
·91 ,, ,, ,,
·70 ,, ,, ,,
·58 ,, ,, ,,
·60 ,, ,, ,,
·32, 15 months (O'CONNOR, 1951)
·73 retest, 15 months (O'CONNOR, 1951)

·96 retest, 15 months (O'CONNOR, 1951)
·89 ,, ,, ,, ,,

60 retest, 15 months (O'CONNOR, 1951)

19	20	21	22	23	24	25	26	27	28	29	30

Significance Levels: $1\% = \cdot254$
$5\% = \cdot195$

	19	20	21	22	23	24	25	26	27	28	29	30
38	—											
33	57	—										
6	−08	−12	—									
4	14	−02	−17	—								
4	−05	−07	16	−48	—							
0	10	−03	01	14	−06	—						
4	16	−12	−01	26	−02	46	—					
1	18	02	06	16	−03	23	65	—				
4	18	20	−14	15	−24	05	−04	01	—			
9	18	−12	05	−03	−04	−09	−03	12	−25	—		
9	11	05	02	32	−25	18	21	13	30	−36	—	

*Table 22. Zero Order Correlation Matrix of Tests in S

7	8	9	10	11	12	13	14	15	16	17	18
—											
26	—										
13	49	—									
-32	-14	00	—								
-32	-08	-14	27	—							
-37	-07	-09	55	30	—						
-45	-09	-11	56	46	51	—					
01	04	04	05	-05	11	-12	—				
02	13	-01	-04	-16	04	-11	72	—			
02	13	-06	-14	-13	-08	00	-30	40	—		
01	-11	09	06	10	04	03	-24	-47	-37	—	
06	-14	00	05	15	06	11	-05	-18	-23	68	—
-23	-10	-07	07	17	10	02	01	-02	-05	-06	-04
05	-12	01	16	15	16	01	-06	-17	-09	02	-03
-02	-14	-10	10	03	01	-05	04	-02	-06	-01	-11
04	19	29	08	-09	-18	00	02	10	07	05	06
-26	-19	-24	16	31	32	24	04	-01	-09	12	11
07	14	15	-02	-02	-21	-02	-05	-02	06	-06	-05
-39	-13	-17	49	20	41	47	-07	09	24	-02	01
-15	-12	-25	28	28	25	30	06	06	03	03	17
-01	-09	-16	00	13	05	06	01	07	08	-06	04
-23	-19	-08	11	06	16	05	-08	-18	-11	06	-10
10	09	11	-04	13	00	-09	-01	01	-05	17	23
-20	-13	-27	05	08	18	14	05	05	04	-04	-04

Variables	No.	1	2	3	4	5	6
Age	1						
Recip. Ponderal Index	2	−17	—				
P.G.R. Index	3	−21	17	—			
Sound Recovery Rate	4	−01	10	−04	—		
Pain Recovery Rate	5	08	05	−06	69	—	
Bowl: Speed	6	−09	07	−03	21	04	—
Bowl: Amount Split	7	03	−05	−05	−15	05	−17
Static Ataxia	8	−02	14	−10	−09	01	−01
Body Sway	9	02	−04	−01	−12	−18	−03
Needle Threading	10	−20	−06	26	−04	−12	01
McDougall-Schuster	11	−02	12	−06	10	04	05
Rail-Walking Test	12	−28	−03	09	02	−05	06
O + P (G.A.T.B.)	13	−26	02	−03	01	−04	04
Resting Pulse	14	−10	−03	06	−01	05	−06
Standing Pulse	15	−18	12	19	01	03	−10
% Incr. Resting to Standing	16	−11	27	17	00	−02	−03
% Incr. to Post-Exercise	17	−04	−05	08	03	−03	05
15-Second Recovery	18	−07	08	17	15	16	−13
Persistence Dynamom.	19	37	−10	−03	26	19	03
Persistence Leg Test (Eysenck)	20	20	−25	10	−03	10	05
Persistence (Maxwell Jones)	21	19	−22	−10	03	08	−05
Modified Maudsley Questionnaire	22	−15	05	17	−06	−09	−03
Dominance Rating	23	−03	−14	05	−03	−09	−16
Anxiety Rating	24	−09	15	−06	06	11	21
Matrices	25	−36	15	29	−04	−13	08
Wechsler Verbal	26	−16	12	21	−08	−05	03
Wechsler Vocabulary	27	−08	−06	04	−04	−04	03
Rated Neurosis	28	25	−14	05	10	−03	12
Unstable History	29	−06	06	−15	23	−03	06
Rated Employment Success	30	09	10	20	−15	−04	−14

the existence of a connection between some one or other of the variables and neurotic tendency.

For fuller discussion of the reasons for the inclusion or exclusion of types of tests, reference can be made to this work, but the main sources can be briefly listed as follows. The need for the inclusion of tests of intelligence may be regarded as so obvious as to require no comment. With defectives, variables measured by tests of intelligence have loomed so large in previous works that other variables have been thought to have played little part in influencing the behaviour of the mentally handicapped. The inclusion of tests of dexterity and co-ordination is justified by direct observation of the behaviour of those defectives who performed in a neurotic fashion on other tests. Included at first because of their direct relationship with employability, they were found in some cases to be related to neurotic tendency. In addition, the work of LUBIN (1951) reported by EYSENCK (1950) and the much earlier work of CULPIN and MAY SMITH with the McDougall Schuster Dotting Machine or Peizograph was held to justify the inclusion of measures of finger and manual dexterity and general locomotor co-ordination. HEATH'S (1942) work with the Rail test was also taken account of in including this measure of locomotor co-ordination, because of its direct relationship with performance in army recruits of low intelligence.

These first two general groups of tests, intelligence and motor, were included because they were directly related to work success, as well as in some cases related indirectly to work success through their relationship with neurotic tendency. Tests of a similar kind, included in the second battery were those of the Speed-choice variety. Such a test was the Bowl Test in which a patient was asked to carry a bowl of water a certain distance in the quickest possible time. He could either go quickly, or go carefully. In addition to being a measure of skill, it was also a measure of choice of kind of performance from slow and careless to fast and careful. No previous example of its use was known at the time of inclusion, but EYSENCK has since drawn attention to the work of ENKE (1930) which showed a connection between performance on this task, neurotic tendency and body build. All such problems which involve generalized motor co-ordination may be supposed to have a theoretical connection with the work of LURIA (1932) in so far as he was able to show the disturbances which affected the movements whether random or co-ordinated, of the emotionally disturbed.

A kindred type of effect may be supposed to underlie autonomic imbalance as measured by the psychogalvanometer. Although the literature is unclear, there has been sufficient work with positive findings, to indicate that a relationship between neurotic tendency and psychogalvanic response exists. FREEMAN and KATZOFF (1942), as well as DARROW and HEATH (1932) may be taken as representatives of this point of view. In a sense such measures take account of responses to stress.

The reaction to stress has always been thought to be one of the subjects wherein fruitful results might be found. Under this heading one might reasonably include tests of persistence and physiological measures of pulse rate and heart rate after exercise. Persistence has been measured by FESSARD *et al* (1933) in this connection with a dynamometer, and by MAXWELL JONES (1944) with a test involving holding one leg up in an uncomfortable position for as long as possible. EYSENCK (1944) has measured it in both ways and like MAXWELL JONES found it to be related to neurosis.

CURETON (1935), and SCHNEIDER and KARPOVICH (1948) have shown that there is a connection between measures of exercise response and performance, and MAXWELL JONES (1948) and HERTZMANN, ORLANSKY and SEITZ (1944) have shown a relationship between measures involving oxygen uptake and blood lactate rise and tendency to neurotic response. Work such as this justified the inclusion of the Step Up test and its associated pulse measures in the form developed by CURETON (1935) in which a patient steps up and down on a chair of standard height and his pulse and pulse recovery rate are measured before and after exercise. McFARLAND and HUDDLESON (1936) have said that such an index of cardiovascular efficiency, "has revealed a significant degree of functional unfitness in the circulatory system of psychoneurotics and psychotic patients".

Complex personality measures are usually either ratings of a trait, or questionnaires concerning behaviour. In these investigations they were included either as cross-checking measures meant to provide initial criteria for other tests, or to illuminate aspects of behaviour for which more objective tests would be either difficult to devise, or too lengthy to administer. Behaviour Scores based on hospital records were also used and are given in full in the Appendix.

A measure of suggestibility was included because EYSENCK'S and FURNEAUX'S (1945) researches have a number of times shown it to be more closely related to neurosis than many other measures used in such investigations. A measure of body build was included despite the comparative failure of this measure when used by other investigators such as BURT (1944) and EYSENCK (1950) because it was thought that defectives might provide a particularly suitable group for investigations in this field. In the first test battery a group of measures was included which was not continued in the second investigation. This group comprised measures of reaction to apparent success or failure. The justification for the inclusion of these measures in the first investigation was the work of HIMMEL-WEIT (1945), but their failure with the defectives in this investigation determined their exclusion from the second study. With defectives in addition the reliabilities of such measures were found to be low, the measure being more characteristic of the social setting in which the test was conducted than of the relatively permanent personality characteristics of the individual patient. Examination of the literature shows that SEARS (1940), GOULD (1939), LEWIN (1942) and SHERIF (1948) adopt a similar view. GOULD (1941) also questions the reliability of the measure and an examination of his work showed that reliabilities lay between 0·04 and 0·57.

Age was included as a variable because of the view frequently taken by psychiatrists working in mental deficiency, that maturity of emotion comes with advancing age in the feeble-minded, and that the disturbances supposed to characterize normal adolescents continue with these patients until about the age of 27. WHITNEY (1948) has expressed this view and says that Elwyn Training School in the United States, acts on this assumption in licensing patients for work outside the institution.

This general justification for the inclusion of various measures, while complete, is not fully descriptive and the reader is referred to the works quoted for a detailed picture of the procedures involved.

The broad inter-relations of the various measures and the criteria can be seen by studying Tables 21 and 22 already set out, and a fuller analysis of results is given in the following section.

Results

Tables 23 and 24 set out the findings of the two investigations and summarize the material available in more detail in the two previous tables. A further table, Table 25, shows the variables which were significant predictors in the two Multiple Regression studies.

Table 23. Relationships between Tests and Criterion of Employment Success (First Investigation)

Variables	Partial r/ Employ-ability	Cumulative Multiple R^2	Beta Weights	Factor Loadings
1. Anx.-Aggress. Rating	35	12	06	53
2. Manual Dext. (u.s.e.s. M + N)	37	26	23	63
3. Finger Dext. (u.s.e.s. O + P)	08	27	02	65
4. Matrices (1938)	11	28	10	56
5. Rail Walking Test	21	33	21	51
6. Leg Persistence Test	−02	33	−03	—
7. Dynamom. Persistence	−03	33	03	−10
8. Body-Sway Test	−20	37	−14	−43
9. Four-Pt. Instab. Rating	−24	42	−29	−54
10. Index of Flexibility	17	45	17	—
11. Speed for Track Tracer	−01	45	−04	−53
12. Goal Discrepancy	06	45	05	—
13. Judgment Discrepancy	02	45	03	−41
14. Index of Responsiveness	02	45	02	09

Column one, in Tables 23 and 24 gives the partial correlation between each variable and the Work Success criterion. Partial correlation here means the extra contribution to the relationship between the criterion and the variable considered, after the effect on this relation of the relation between the criterion and each

Table 24. Relationship between Tests and Criterion of Employment Success (Second Investigation)

Variables	Partial r/Employ-ability	Cumu-lative R^2	Beta Weights	Factor Loadings 1	2	3
1. Age	09	01	09	−31	−45	−23
2. Recip. Ponderal Index	11	02	19			
3. P.G.R. Index	21	07	10	26	04	15
4. Sound Recovery Rate	−15	09	−19	15	03	10
5. Pain Recovery Rate	08	09	12			
6. Bowl: Speed	−09	10	−08	13	17	29
7. Bowl: Amount Split	−25	16	−10	−55	−13	−05
8. Static Ataxia						
9. Body Sway				−31	30	27
10. Needle Threading	04	17	00			
11. McDougall-Schuster	−02	17	14	50	−02	−13
12. Rail-Walking Test				61	−12	−19
13. O +P (U.S.E.S.)				62	07	−06
14. Resting Pulse	−05	18	−11			
15. Standing Pulse	04	18	05			
16. % Incr. Resting to Standing	03	18	−02			
17. % Incr. Standing to Post-Exercise	29	27	−01			
18. 15-Second Recovery	−10	28	02	16	19	−02
19. Persistence Dynamom.				16	−40	−10
20. Persistence Leg Test (Eysenck)				−09	−35	−19
21. Persistence (Maxwell Jones)	04	29	12			
22. Modified Maudsley Questionnaire	23	35	23	−07	33	35
23. Dominance Rating	−18	38	−11			
24. Anxiety Rating			08	−11	45	54
25. Matrices (1938)			04	66	08	09
26. Wechsler Verbal			09	51	01	−08
27. Wechsler Vocabulary			21			
28. Rated Neurosis			−23	16	−45	−11
29. Unstable History			10	−01	34	05
30. Rated Employment Success				28	−47	−27

previous variable has been abstracted. The next column is the simple addition of each successive squared partial correlation in the previous column, thus providing at the bottom a cumulative correlation of the battery with the chosen criterion. This is Employment Success in both Tables 23 and 24. Column three gives the Beta Weights appropriate to all variables and the succeeding columns

Table 25

BEST INDEPENDENT PREDICTORS OF
EMPLOYMENT SUCCESS

First Investigation	*Second Investigation*
Instability Measure	Instability Measure
Manual Dexterity Test	Rated Dominance

OTHER VARIABLES CLOSELY RELATED
WITH EMPLOYMENT SUCCESS

Anxiety Measure	Anxiety Measure
Locomotor or Rail Test of Ability	Diagnosed Neurosis
Body Sway Suggestibility	Level of Psychogalvanic Reaction

in each table show the results of the Factor Analyses. By comparing the results for the first investigation with those for the second we find that ratings of past behaviour or history of past socially unacceptable behaviour are the best indicators of subsequent success at work. In the second study the exclusion of some of the best predictors from the first study by reason of overlap in the sample probably reduces the predicting power of the battery. However, despite this, the multiple correlation with the criterion is 0·62 as compared with 0·67 for the first battery.

In this study individual findings worthy of attention are the relatively close relationship between measures of intelligence and measures of manual dexterity. This finding, first noted by ATTEN-BOROUGH and FARBER (1934) in this country, and ABEL (1925) in America, is most strongly confirmed in this study by the relationship between needle threading and the Matrices test. Neither this test nor the McDougall Schuster Dotting Test showed the relationship with diagnosed neurosis which has been found among normally intelligent subjects. This is not to say that a different pattern would not emerge if the group were given long training on an individual task such as the McDougall Schuster. In such a case, the correlation with intelligence might change considerably. Subsequent work showed that training has more effect on unstable patients than on stable.

The degree to which the dominant role of intelligence in this group affects the way in which the prediction of neurotic disposition is accomplished can be seen in the above example and also in the way in which the test of primary suggestibility, body sway, is found to be associated as much with verbal intelligence (Wechsler) as with unstable history. Most of the measures of balance or performance come out in this direction with this particular group of patients. More orthodox findings which are more nearly in accord with personality theory about the relation between neurosis and poor work response are found with the persistence tests. The same tends to be true of the psychogalvanic responses to stress, although results are not so positive as to leave no doubt. On the whole the measures of exercise response do not show up as closely related to neurosis or problem behaviour, nor is body build found to be related to neurosis in the form in which the test was administered. Age, however, is fairly strongly related to diagnosed neurosis. In so far as these findings repeat those of the first investigation, they confirm them, with the notable exception of body sway suggestibility. However, the degree of association between the tests changed markedly from one investigation to the other.

The best prediction of work success in the first battery were an instability rating and a measure of manual dexterity, the Peg board. If, instead of a rating which is likely to have a low reliability, one substitutes an objective test, i.e. one objectively measurable, an almost equally successful prediction can be accomplished with the Rail Walking test and the Body Sway test. However, as shown in the second study, an apparently reliable group as these two appeared to be on paper did not hold up when repeated in the second investigation. Despite this it remains true that a relationship between emotional stability and capacity to succeed at manual work has been established with a feeble-minded group of male adolescents. What has been least successful in these studies has been the search for a clearly defined objective measure of neurotic tendency in the feeble-minded. So far ratings have been more successful predictors than more objective tests, although their reliability has been lower.

However, having established in the overall similarity of trend of the two studies, that emotional instability is the most serious cause of occupational disability among the feeble-minded, it must be made clear that the stability of the results ends there. In detail the two sets of findings are very dissimilar. If a comparison is made of the first 104 results with the half of the second group who were not involved in the first study, this stands out in a striking fashion.

A simple way of doing this was used which consisted of deriving Beta Weights for the variables in the first study and applying these to the scores obtained by the newly tested sample tested on the same variables. A resulting set of predictions of the criterion were obtained. A cross-check on the finding was carried out by using Factor Loadings in the place of Beta Weights. The results obtained are summarized in Tables 26 (*a*) and (*b*).

Table 26 (*a*). *Multiple Correlations of those Variables with the Criterion*

First Investigation	Second Investigation	
·61	·25	(with B weights)
·52	·25	(with factor loading)

Table 26 (*b*). *Zero Order Correlations for First and Second Batteries*

		1	2	3	4
Rail	1				
Body Sway	2	−09			
Matrices	3	20	−24		
Criterion	4	44	−33	34	

		1	2	3	4
Rail	1				
Body Sway	2	−18			
Matrices	3	58	−24		
Criterion	4	25	−14	26	

Three variables only were used in this study and intercorrelated with the criterion in each case. There were the Body Sway Test of Primary Suggestibility, the Progressive Matrices Test and Heath Rail Walking Test of Locomotor Co-ordination (1942). These tests were used because they were objective, relatively reliable, and clear indicators of different psychological constituents of behaviour. The fact that the multiple correlation with the criterion dropped markedly from about 0·6 or 0·5 to 0·25 when the old

Weights were applied to the new data reflects the possible variability of findings based on common well standardized tests. Table 26(*b*) shows the two sets of zero order correlations on which the calculations were based. The differences in these correlations show why the multiple correlations changed so markedly. Theoretically the change must be held to be due to the unreliability both of the tests and of the measure of work success, or to limited sampling of patients as well as the selection of tests based on such limited sampling and the sampling error involved.

It would be impossible to say as a result of this obvious variability, that the characteristics measured by these tests were invariant. On the other hand, the size of the two groups of patients used prevents us from asserting that differences between the relationships of the traits measured by the tests are due to chance. The criterion of work success for example is the most unreliable of the variables involved. Relative reliabilities can be seen from Tables 21 and 22. The picture is therefore inconclusive so far as the predictive value of the tests involved is concerned.

The main body of the data of both studies still enables us to infer that emotional instability is important in occupational success with this group of patients. Such an inference is strengthened when the test results of 10 very successful and 10 very unsuccessful boys chosen at random are compared. The picture of the successful patient is of an adolescent with a history of good behaviour in the hospital, irrespective of supervisor or nurse, a person of good persistence as measured on test, an individual who may have been slightly longer in the hospital, who has a good exercise tolerance on the step up test and whose reaction to noise as measured by Psychogalvanic Reflex is relatively slight. Such a successful patient shows less anxiety than the unsuccessful and is faster at a speed-accuracy choice task, as well as more dexterous and coordinated in his movements. A further investigation with a mechanical task repeated over a period of time, showed that such a person was operating nearer his ceiling of performance and therefore was less likely to show rapid improvement than his more unstable fellow. Such a summary presents a not inaccurate and succinct description of the differences in performance which may be occasioned by instability in patients of this level of intelligence.

A further analysis of the findings enables us to say that severe neurosis as judged both by test and clinical judgment is rare in this kind of patient if DEWAN'S (1948) findings are to be thought representative. So far as can be judged either on the basis of psychiatric rating or objective test, severe neurotic handicap is likely to occur in about the same proportions as those reported by RUSSELL FRASER for a war-time factory population, that is, about 10 per cent. In the case of these two investigations the figures centred round 6 per cent in the first investigation and 12 per cent in the second. Mild neurotic tendency was found to be present in about twice as many cases as found in a factory population, that is, in about 40 per cent of patients. However, the experiment which showed the relatively rapid improvement of the unstable boys on a routine task suggests that such mild handicap may not be a serious bar to productivity in all cases. The more recent work of MARKOWE and BARBER (1953) seems to show conclusions of a similar kind.

Conclusions

The conclusions which may be drawn from such data are that it is inadvisable to try to select patients for trial in cases where uncertainty exists, although severe cases will certainly need special treatment and training over and above that usually given, if their success is to be prolonged. It may be inferred that only a limited number of patients are seriously handicapped by emotional instability however, and that for the remainder, the degree of handicap is not so great that it will seriously affect their working life, providing supervision is informed and not autocratic. Further evidence on this question will be given in the next chapter. Mild handicap may even disappear so far as speed of work is concerned and the emotionally unstable achieve speeds and levels of adjustment equivalent to the more stable.

Under these circumstances, it would be wise except in severe cases of disturbance, to give all feeble-minded boys a trial at simple repetitive work rather than to exclude them on this ground and to attempt some selection which at present must be based on unreliable tests and criteria, and lead to hardship and injustice for the patients. The severely handicapped neurotic defective is, however, a clear case for exclusion from work until he has been given preparatory treatment and training. The beginnings of such a therapy are described in Chapter 9.

Finally, it may be said that whatever is true of neurotics of average intelligence, the neurotic feeble-minded patient seems to show a temperament change with age. BINET noted such a temperament alteration. With defectives, therefore, we may call in question the relative invariability of personality traits and of degrees of skill so far as these are affected by personality.

Thus the thesis that neurosis is a major obstacle to the employment of the feeble-minded must be regarded with reserve. An incapacity at the age of 16 may not continue in later years, although there will be a small percentage of cases 6 per cent to 12 per cent in whom tests show a degree of neurotic tendency for which special treatment should be recommended.

G

CHAPTER SIX

STUDIES OF TRAINING AND OCCU-PATION OF HIGH-GRADE DEFECTIVES

THE FUNCTIONS of the mental deficiency colony are, on the one hand, to look after those defectives who need long-stay care, and, on the other hand, to rehabilitate defectives whose main needs are for social and occupational training and education in the broadest sense. In preceding chapters an attempt has been made to show the distribution of defectives by sex, age, grade and psychological qualities. In this and subsequent chapters present training policy is discussed and our own studies and those of our colleagues are described.

Present Training Policy in Hospitals

One function of the mental-deficiency institutions is to train patients to work, and if possible to train them for work in the community. Since, as has been shown, large numbers of patients in institutions are dull, rather than *cognitively* defective, the institution regimen should be adapted to meet their needs and provide for their potentialities of development. An examination of institutional training policy, particularly as it affects high-grade patients, enables some assessment to be made of how far this is the case. It should of course be remembered that the great majority of these so-called high-grade patients are not sick—they are, rather, dullards and simpletons in need of care, supervision, or control either because they are unable to look after themselves and have families who are believed to be incapable of doing so, or, in a small minority of cases, because they are a danger to the community owing to their anti-social conduct. In so far as their social incompetence is based on characteristics which are subject to training (such as occupational competence and ability to keep a job, literacy, socially acceptable behaviour, conformity with the law), their deficiencies are not incurable. Indeed as PENROSE (1949) has pointed out, high-grade institutional defectives can best be regarded as being a tiny sample of individuals selected for special care (partly because of social factors for which they are by no means responsible) from a much larger population of individuals who are biologically their equals but who are regarded in law as normal citizens. These latter for the most part manage their lives satisfactorily in the community, and it is suggested that the majority of "defectives" could also be trained to do so.

The information obtained in the London Survey described in Chapter 3 shows the distribution of patients in institutions by occupation. Among the feeble-minded 51 out of 240 patients, or more than one-fifth of the sample, were working in hospital workshops, while 81, or one-third, were working in the wards or as domestic servants in the hospital.

The kind of work done by patients working in hospital workshops was well described by BICKMORE, in 1913, in a book dealing with the training of mental defectives, and it must be added that though exceptions are to be found, much of BICKMORE'S description would apply equally well to many mental-deficiency hospitals today. Work done includes the following: carpentry, bookbinding, envelope-making, box-making, tin-smithing, tailoring, upholstering and mattress-making, printing, needlework, painting, building, wood-chopping and bundling, and shoe-repairing. The titles of some of these occupations give little idea of the character of the work performed; and the teaching methods of the trainers, and the equipment used in the workshops, are often extremely old-fashioned. Only in the protected environment of a hospital could these uneconomical and outmoded methods continue.

Elsewhere (TIZARD and O'CONNOR, 1952), the following specific criticisms of much of the occupational training have been made:

1. Most of the training is designed to give the patients something to do rather than to employ them on work of value to the community. In times of severe and chronic unemployment, when very few defectives can be sent on licence to the community, and when public policy deems it expedient for institutions not to compete in any sense with private employers, this is readily understandable. In times of full employment and general shortages a different attitude to the training of defectives seems advisable.

2. The work done in institution workshops bears almost no relation to the types of job which defectives do when on licence.

A mere handful of those who are trained so laboriously on the skilled and semi-skilled operations learn to perform them competently enough to be able to obtain work as artisans in the community. The bulk of defectives can obtain employment only on less skilled work.

3. The equipment used in institution workshops is almost without exception obsolete as far as industry is concerned. Much work which is done commercially by machine is done by hand, or for the most part by the most primitive of machines. Little is done to speed up production to the tempo required to keep a job in the community, and the defectives get no experience in handling machines, and so becoming accustomed to them. Consequently output remains low, and even though labour is free the selling costs are often higher than commercial selling costs, which are reduced by the economies of large-scale buying and by efficient machine production. This factor of economic cost is obscured in the annual reports of some institutions which give "turnover figures" but not a profit-and-loss balance-sheet of workshop expenses.

4. Little contact is made with commercial firms which might be induced to take numbers of defectives who have already received some training, into their own factories. Thus, in many hospitals, a potential stepping-stone to life in the community is not made use of.

5. The work is too often carried out in an atmosphere devoid of incentives. Neither the Wood Report nor BICKMORE (1913) mention monetary rewards—assuming apparently that praise and blame from an instructor are sufficient for defectives. But the absence of monetary rewards in some hospitals makes the problem of providing incentives a difficult one, and also prevents patients from learning the value of money. Unless those who will probably be sent on licence in the future are given more money to spend while they are in institutions, they are unlikely to learn from their own mistakes how money can be wasted, and what money can buy.

6. Too little attention has been paid to the selection and training of supervisors and training staff. Because of the low status of the job and, in general, the poor working conditions and pay, it is difficult to attract skilled craftsmen to act as trainers in mental-

deficiency workshops. Few of those who are appointed have had any experience with or knowledge of the social and psychological problems which arise in institutions and in dealing with the sub-normal. Nor are they given any instruction as a rule, once they are appointed. Policy in regard to social and occupational aspects of the mental deficiency services is in need of review.

7. The supervision of patients in daily service, or on licence, is often inadequate. Some hospitals still have no trained social workers at all, and few have more than one or two. Where there are no social workers, nurses are expected to carry out the necessary placement and supervision of patients in daily service, and, except where this duty is delegated to the Local Authority's Mental Health Officer, of those on licence. Because of the very great shortage of nurses, if for no other reason, this is not a task which can be left to them to carry out in addition to their other duties. To be effective, the supervision and placement of institutional defectives demands the efforts of suitably qualified staff with enough time for the frequent visiting of cases that require it.

An Experimental Workshop

It was noted in the Wood Report that many defectives who would fail at complex or difficult tasks might be able to succeed at simple repetitive work. Two problems must, however, be distinguished. Nearly all high-grade mentally defective adults who are not handicapped by severe physical disabilities could probably learn to do the operations required in, for example, simple factory work. But many appear to lack the persistence which would enable them to work quickly for long periods of time. For this reason and because of the widespread belief that under factory conditions the simple-minded are often taken advantage of or led into trouble, little attempt has been made to train institutional patients for the only kind of work which many of them appear likely to be able to do in an industrial community. The factors influencing success and failure at work of this kind seemed however to be worth investigating, and we were fortunate in being able, through the courtesy and collaboration of Dr. J. K. Collier Laing and the Darenth and Stone Hospital Management Committee, to set up an experimental workshop to examine problems of industrial training at

Darenth Park. Darenth is a large comprehensive colony for adult defectives which contains about 2,000 patients of both sexes. It was built in 1878 as a school for imbecile children but gradually became an institution housing defectives of all types. Since 1934 it has admitted only patients over the age of 16 years (LAING, 1952). It is situated in the country, near Dartford, Kent, and until the coming into operation of the National Health Service Act was administered by the London County Council primarily as a centre for high-grade defective adults.

Workshop investigations were begun in January 1950 and studies were continued at Darenth Park during 1950 and 1951. Other investigations have since been carried out at the Manor Hospital, Epsom, Surrey, where we have enjoyed the hospitality of Dr. J. F. MACMAHON, Physician Superintendent of the Manor, and his Committee, and have been able to collaborate with Dr. A. D. B. CLARKE and Dr. A. M. CLARKE, psychologists at that institution since 1951.

The workshops at Darenth were established to carry out experimental studies of occupational training of high-grade adolescent and adult defectives, to discover suitable conditions for the running of training workshops, and to determine the value of the training given in them. This we did by comparing the success in the community of those who passed through the experimental workshops with that of other patients who had the ordinary hospital training. Although the number of adult female patients resident in institutions for the mentally defective is actually slightly larger than the number of males, almost all of our experimental work has been carried out with male patients. Difficulties in securing for female patients the conditions which would make it possible to employ them in work of the kind we were interested in prevented us from exploring the extent to which changes in an institutional regimen would result in changes in the behaviour of mentally defective women.*

In order to ensure that the jobs done in the training workshops were similar to what is actually done in industry, work was subcontracted from outside firms. This policy had the advantage of

---

* Such studies are at present being made by Dr. CLARKE at the Manor Hospital.

enabling patients later to be placed in jobs for which they had already been trained, and enabled us to pay the patients trade union piece rates for their work.

Before we looked for work, criteria were drawn up which took account of the need both to train the patients for industrial work and to obtain quantitative measures of output for experimental purposes. The following conditions were finally thought desirable:

1. The work should be repetitive.

2. Patients should be employed on one job for periods long enough to enable experimental studies lasting many weeks to be carried out.

3. Individual piecework in which speed was controlled by the operator and not mechanically or by others should be obtained.

4. Machines should not be used.

5. The work should not involve fine movements and should be able to be easily checked.

6. All operatives should be employed on the same job.

The decision that hand work rather than machine work should be undertaken was made by the hospital authorities. (Under certain circumstances simple machine work in which recognized safety precautions were observed appears very suitable for the employment of high-grade defectives.) Reasons for imposing the other criteria need no comment.

Because all work had to be carried from a factory to the hospital and back it was necessary to have items which were not bulky. To ensure that the patients were given incentives related to their output and to offset charges of sweated labour, trade union piece rates were paid.

Help in obtaining work was sought from the Ministry of Labour and the Regional Psychiatrist to the South East Metropolitan Region, Dr. R. F. TREDGOLD, and two large firms were found willing to sub-contract work. One job which was done was the filing of rough edges from moulded plastic objects and another the folding and glueing of cardboard boxes. In the case of the boxes the packaging for delivery to the customer was eventually entrusted to the patients in the workshop.

96   The Social Problem of Mental Deficiency

The Unit was provided by the hospital with at first one, and subsequently a second workshop, each capable of housing about 80 workers. Sixteen youths were employed at first and the number then increased gradually until there were about 60 working in the shops at the end of the first year. Hours worked were arranged to fit in with the hospital programme: they were 8.30 a.m. to 12.00 noon, and 1.30 p.m. to 4.30 p.m. on weekdays, and 8.30 a.m. to 12.30 p.m. on Saturdays, a total of 36½ hours a week.

We were interested in the employability of young, high-grade defectives, and the first patients were all classified as feeble-minded. Many of them were delinquents, not readily employable in the institution workshops.

A number of difficulties were encountered in the early stages of the workshop investigation. These proved instructive and will, accordingly, be described in some detail.

(a) Though it had been intended that we should select the patients to go into the shops from among those tested in the initial survey, only half of the patients were chosen by us, the remainder being added by the Chief Male Nurse. Of the sixteen patients who first began to work in the workshop, six were awaiting resident licence. These were in consequence not interested in the work in the shops which to them meant filling in time until the formalities of licence were completed. An additional five of the original sixteen were excitable, boisterous youths who were considered too unstable to continue in the shops and who were consequently dismissed. (Later, when a routine had been established and the shops were working normally, four of these boys were again placed in the shops and settled down well.) We learned from this that one should begin such an investigation with a few carefully chosen patients, and that only when things were going satisfactorily should one attempt to build up the numbers or add difficult patients.

(b) The supply of work at first was irregular, and payment was held up because the hospital was unable to advance money owed by the firms but not paid out.

(c) The boys had no realistic appreciation of what was required of them, or what they could expect to get out of the shop. Hence they expected at once too much and too little. When the first payment of 5 shillings for part of the first week's work was made they were all, except for one boy who had worked in the community for a number of years, amazed and delighted. On the other hand, when a wireless was installed in the shop they objected strenuously every time it was turned off.

(*d*) The initial difficulties made the boys very suspicious of the whole project. They were incredulous about wages, and tended to regard the shop as an alternative to, and not a step towards, daily licence. It was only when a number of boys had gone from the shop to daily licence at one of the firms from which the work was sent, that these initial suspicions of the project weakened.

(*e*) It was difficult to get the boys to come on time, and to prevent them from wandering off to the canteen half way through the morning, as they were accustomed to in the other institution workshops. Only when the shops had been established for two or three months was good work routine established which made it possible to introduce high-spirited patients into them with any hope that they would settle down.

(*f*) Following the Hawthorne investigators (ROETHLISBERGER and DICKSON 1949), we planned an ambitious half-hourly check on production. This was quite unsuccessful, and caused a great deal of avoidable confusion before it was decided to drop it.

(*g*) Several other factors added to our early difficulties. The weather was extremely cold and the shops inadequately heated for some time until new radiators could be installed. Again, we ourselves did not appreciate the standards required by the firms for work to be accepted. These standards, it seemed, depended very much upon the attitude of the checkers at the firm. It was only when the nurses in charge of the workshop got on friendly terms with the inspectors at the firms, that work began to be passed by them.

Finally the firms sent, and continued to send, a large number of different types of job to be done. It took some time for both us and them to understand what work was suitable and for them to plan to send us large orders and not small ones.

In general, it may be said, the project was planned too ambitiously. We hoped to be able to get it going rapidly, so that experimental variations might be introduced a few weeks after the shops were opened. In the end it was nearly eight months before the shops were running smoothly enough, and before we had enough nursing assistance to plan our first experiment. During these months, however, we gained not only valuable administrative experience, but insight into the expectations and the frustrations of high-grade institutional defectives.

The administration of the workshops and the supervision of patients employed in them were from the outset undertaken by hospital nurses. Those allotted to duties in the shops at that time were among the ablest members of the hospital nursing staff, and some of them had had a considerable amount of industrial experience themselves. Much of the success of the project was due to the efficient manner in which they carried out their duties and to the fact that there were, during the first year, between three and five members of the nursing staff engaged in the workshop, under the full-time, and later the part-time direction of an assistant chief male nurse, Mr. H. A. YAKES.

Statistics collected at the end of 1951 give an idea of the success achieved as judged by the ability of patients who passed through the workshops to succeed on daily licence in the community.

During 1950 and 1951 a total of 194 patients were employed in the workshops; but many of them had been there for only a short period of time when the census was made. Sixty had been tried on licence. Some of the patients went from the workshops to one of the firms subcontracting work (Kolster-Brandes of Sidcup). Others went to other work for which they had had no special training. In December 1951, their distribution was as follows:

From workshops to daily licence and succeeded on their first trial	36
From workshops to daily licence and succeeded after being unsuccessfully placed	5
Tried unsuccessfully on daily licence	19
Dismissed or removed from workshops (not tried on daily licence)	25
From workshops to resident licence with their parents	3
In workshops but not tried on licence	106
Total	194

Of those sent on licence, Table 27 shows the success and failure of patients tried at Kolster-Brandes (K.B.) and at other types of employment. Though the numbers are not large, there is a significant difference between the proportion of patients successfully placed with K.B. as compared with that of boys placed elsewhere. This is believed to be due not only to the training received but also to the type of supervision given at a large firm where patients were under the charge of an exceptionally capable and understanding supervisor. We are unable to determine the extent to which each of these factors contributed to the boys' success on licence, but there is little doubt about the success itself. The boys seemed to benefit both by working alongside normal employees and by remaining in company with others whom they knew.

Table 27. Successes and Failures as between K.B. and Other Forms of Daily Licence (excluding two boys tried both at K.B. and in other forms of employment)

	Daily Licence			
	Successes	Failures	Total	Percentage failure
K.B.	27	6	33	18
Other	14	11	25	44
Total	41	17	58	

$X^2 = 4.58$ p$<$·05

Between the beginning of May and the end of July 1950 the average weekly wage of 24 boys employed in the shops was just over 27 shillings a week for a $36\frac{1}{2}$ hour week. The shops as a whole earned £1,250 in the first eight months, and £2,750 in just over a year.

During 1951 on the completion of our experimental studies, the hospital undertook full control of the workshops which were re-organized under the name of the Social Readjustment Centre. For administrative reasons the wage system was changed and the incentive bonuses were scaled down. In the middle of 1952 the average wage of patients working in the shops was 6s. 8d. a week, the range being 2s. 6d. to 15s. with 2s. 6d. bonus for those who had worked best in each of the shops during the week. Outings for patients were still arranged and the youths who began work on licence were fitted out with clothes, half the cost of which was met directly out of their earnings, and half taken either from the pool of undistributed earnings (which also were used to pay for the outings) or from the hospital amenity fund. All money earned was still distributed to the patients; but it might be thought that more was being arranged *for* them and that the relationship between what they did by their own efforts and the rewards and privileges they achieved was less obvious than formerly.

These changes were in part brought about through administrative difficulties and alterations. A larger proportion of lower-grade patients was employed in the Social Readjustment Centre than was engaged in the training workshops so that their function was somewhat modified. In 1952 between 130 and 140 patients in all were employed. Owing to staffing shortages, they were under the supervision of three nursing assistants (two of them retired men who had come back to the hospital to assist in the running of the centre). The assistant chief male nurse was still nominally responsible for the general running of the scheme.

Summary and Conclusions

It will be evident that the theoretical ideas underlying the workshop investigation outlined above were very simple ones. Large numbers of adolescents and adults in mental deficiency institutions must be regarded as dull normal persons who, because they are somewhat unstable, or have no homes, or need more care than is given them in the homes they have, come to require a period of institutional care. It is in the interests both of these patients, and of the community, that their stay in institutions should not be unduly prolonged. While it is possible that an entirely different form of care might be more appropriate to their needs, it is also true that even within the present institutional framework, without really adequate social assistance and educational services, their reablement can be quite effectively achieved if they are given training in habits of work on simple jobs, and some instruction in how to look after money. For some of these patients routine industrial work appears to be the most suitable form of job-training, though others, especially the strong and well-built, often prefer, and are more suited to, labouring jobs. The Darenth Park investigation was undertaken to see how much could be done to rehabilitate defectives under existing forms of institutional care. A further evaluation of its success is given in Chapter 8.

CHAPTER SEVEN

EXPERIMENTAL STUDIES OF OCCUPATIONAL TRAINING AND OF EDUCATION

THE RESEARCH described in the last chapter showed that under suitable conditions many patients could be trained to undertake successfully work which is done commercially by hand workers in industry. We endeavoured also to investigate some of the main factors responsible for successful adaptation to work. Four studies are reported below. The results have suggested some possible lines of policy which might be explored in mental deficiency hospitals today, and have pointed to further problems for research. The first of these studies—that of types of supervision and their effects on patients in hospital workshops—was carried out at Darenth Park in 1950. The three later investigations, one concerned with teaching defectives to read, and the other two with incentives and skills, were carried out at the Manor Hospital in 1952.

THE FOUR INVESTIGATIONS

1. *The Supervision Investigation*

The kind of supervision given to patients is a factor of great importance in dealing with high-grade, often unstable defectives. Accordingly, an experiment was carried out to investigate the effects of different kinds of supervision upon production and behaviour in the workshops. The study of "social climate" by LIPPITT and his colleagues (LIPPITT, 1940; LIPPITT and WHITE, 1947) provided a starting point for our investigation, which, however, differed from theirs in a number of ways. Three types of supervision were investigated: they were called "strict supervision" in which criticism was given for misbehaviour and poor work but no praise for work well done, "friendly supervision" in which praise was given whenever possible and the supervisor mixed with the boys in a friendly way, and "*laissez-faire* supervision" in which the supervisor took little interest in the shop and busied himself with his own affairs. A full description of the study is available elsewhere (TIZARD, 1953*a*).

Three nurses acted as supervisors; they were capable and versatile men and were selected by the Chief Male Nurse as being among the best nurses he had available at the time. The subjects were 36 high grade defectives (age 19·00 ±4·41 years, Wechsler Verbal I.Q. 68·00 ±9·57 points, Matrices Raw Score 26·09 ±9·43 points). During the 12 weeks of the experiment they were employed on the two types of work being subcontracted—hand-trimming and box folding.

The experiment was divided into three periods of four weeks each. Boys were ranked according to their previous production and split into three matched groups, each of which went to a separate shop under the control of its own supervisor. One nurse served in each shop during each period and practised one of the three types of supervision. After each period of four weeks the nurses changed shops, and also changed the type of supervision they were carrying out. (The design of the experiment was thus modelled on a Graeco-Latin Square.) Detailed instructions laying down rules of behaviour to be followed in each of the three types of supervision were given to the nurses, and these were discussed with them before the experiment began. A meeting took place after work on most days during the experiment, at which incidents occurring during the day and general problems of interest were discussed with the nurses.* These meetings helped them to standardize their roles.

Throughout the experiment each nurse served in each shop, adopting a different kind of supervision in each; each shop was supervised by each nurse in turn and was given each of the three kinds of supervision.

Observations of the behaviour of both patients and nurses were made by the experimenters. Of the many techniques tried out, which included ratings, measures of the quantity and quality of

---

* The nurses were Mr. A. H. WILSON, Mr. R. L. TYAS and Mr. M. P. WHITE. They spent their time as follows:

    Nurse 1—1st month, Shop 1 (*Strict*); 2nd month, Shop 2 (*Laissez-faire*); 3rd month, Shop (*Friendly*).

    Nurse 2—1st month, Shop 2 (*Friendly*); 2nd month, Shop 3 (*Strict*); 3rd month, Shop 1 (*Laissez-faire*).

    Nurse 3—1st month, Shop 3 (*Laissez-faire*); 2nd month, Shop 1 (*Friendly*); 3rd month, Shop 2 (*Strict*).

production, diaries and "time sampling" observations, the qualitative measures and the time sampling were the most useful. A ten-second interval was adopted for time sampling "Industriousness" and "Talkativeness" throughout the experiment.

Industriousness was measured on a three-point scale. If a boy worked steadily throughout a ten-second observation period he was scored 2. If he had a break of up to five seconds, duration he was scored 1. If he worked five seconds or less during the interval he was scored 0. Scores were summed at the end of each day.

Talkativeness was assessed on a two-point scale. If a boy talked during an observation period he was scored 1; if he did not talk he was scored zero.

Twelve ten-second time samplings were made each day. The order in which the shops were visited was varied and scores were averaged to allow for the effects of absence.

As has been found by other investigators, we found that the boys took little or no notice of the time sampling after the first few days. No explanations of our behaviour were given.

At the end of the experiment the quantitative scores were statistically treated by analysis of variance. The results showed marked and consistent differences between Strict and Friendly supervision on the one hand and *Laissez-faire* supervision on the other, but there was little to differentiate the two more active types of supervision.

Some of the qualitative findings seemed to us of interest. Two points will be discussed: differences between types of supervision and the problem of training supervisors.

Differences between Types of Supervision

These were greatest during the first month before the nurses had begun to feel the strain of role-playing. Though the majority of patients behaved well under strict supervision, anxious or neurotic patients responded very badly. (One developed a facial dermatitis during the first month which cleared up during the following month when he was under friendly supervision, another ran away, and two others became more and more dejected as the month went on.) Under friendly supervision also the majority of patients behaved well, though some tough-minded patients took advantage of what they regarded as weakness on the part of the supervisor. Only the very stable continued to work conscientiously under *laissez-faire* supervision. These findings were not un-expected.

There was also evidence to suggest that it was the brighter patients who in the judgment of the supervisors and the investi-gators needed the strictest supervision. Whether this was because they were inherently more unstable, or because they were bored by the hospital routine and the lack of interesting things to do, we could not determine from our findings. It seemed probable that while some were unstable the majority were merely bored.

The Training of Supervisors

The experiment was not designed to test hypotheses affecting the training of supervisors. But in the course of it three nurses were observed closely over a period of three months under different conditions, and prior to the experiment other nurses had been observed for shorter periods while doing duty in the workshops. Arising out of this experience, over a period of more than a year, some observations on problems affecting supervisors and their training will be made.

(i) *The need for good supervisors*—Nearly all of the boys who have been employed in the workshops have responded well to good supervisors. The ease with which the carry-over from *laissez-faire* to strict supervision was effected during the second month of the experiment demonstrated this. And when, on two or three occa-sions a firm called for work to be returned quickly and the boys were asked to make a special effort, the response was always excellent. There are very few high-grade defective adolescents who are not anxious to be well thought of and to please. Under a poor supervisor, however, the boys very rapidly got out of control. The conditions under *laissez-faire* supervision were not very different from those which had cropped up from time to time prior to the experiment under some of the nurses who had been sent to the shops. Some nurses allowed arguing, swearing, and, on one or two occasions, even fighting to go on without checking it. Sometimes this seemed due to apathy on the part of the nurse, more often to lack of experience.

H

(ii) *Establishing good rapport*—Because their emotional needs are often unsatisfied, and because a nurse is often the only person to whom a boy can turn for advice, good rapport between nurse and boy is desirable. If a supervisor is friendly this can easily be obtained. But under strict supervision boys did not bring their personal problems to the nurse. There was an indication during the experiment that they were unwilling to approach *laissez-faire* supervisors also, and the nurses discussed whether there was more contact between nurse and boy under strict than under *laissez-faire* supervision. (No agreement was reached; in any replication of this experiment some attempt should be made to decide this point.)

(iii) *Changes in supervision*—Since a nurse may often be handling a boy in the wrong manner it seems desirable that where possible more than one supervisor should be engaged in supervision duties. On the other hand, frequent changes in supervision have an unsettling effect, and nurses on shift work may not be the best people to carry out supervision duties.

(iv) *Communication from staff to patients*—The hierarchical character of a mental deficiency hospital makes discussion among nurses of different rank extraordinarily difficult. The communication of orders and instructions to patients is perhaps even more unsatisfactory. To promise a patient something which one is not then able to carry out is regarded as a grave mistake for a mental nurse, and it is in consequence a common practice to tell patients as little as possible about any plans for their future, or about any changes in administration which may involve them. This makes it impossible for subnormal boys to set themselves long-term objectives, or to work towards specific goals (e.g. parole, daily licence, transfer from a closed to an open ward).

(v) *The training of supervisors*—The previous remarks suggest some of the chief difficulties that would have to be overcome if a programme for training supervisors was to be attempted. At present very little is done in the training of student nurses to see that they get adequately supervised experience in handling the social problems associated with the training of mental defectives. The training of mental deficiency nurses is largely concerned with medical matters—insufficient time is often given to psychological or social matters, and there is little corresponding to the practical instruction given to school teachers in training, or to officer cadets. In institution workshops the supervision is normally done by tradesmen who need have no interest in psychology or in teaching subnormal patients the social skills they require so badly. Our experience suggests that nurses on the whole are better qualified to undertake the supervision duties necessary for sheltered workshops than are the present trainers. But the training of nurses does not always give them the practice they need in order to carry out such duties as well as they might.

It would be an easy matter to devise a training syllabus which did include both practical and theoretical training of the sort that is required. The Hawthorne practice (ROETHLISBERGER and DICKSON) of training foremen by means of hypothetical case studies, which were discussed by groups of foremen under a personnel officer, could easily be adapted to meet the needs of mental deficiency practice. This, coupled with practical experience with groups of defectives both at work and at play, would prove a valuable addition to the training of all who were engaged in mental-deficiency nursing. But, to be effective, the periods of instruction would need to be formally incorporated in the training syllabus.

2. *The Second Investigation—Teaching Defectives to Read*

Psychometric investigations of the intelligence of the feeble-minded with whom we were working showed the average I.Q. on Binet or Wechsler tests to be approximately 70 points. The average "mental age" of the patients was therefore about ten years. The median reading age of 100 patients tested on the Schonell mechanical reading scale, which has been very soundly standardized on army recruits, was however only 8·6 years, and the distribution of reading ages, given in Table 28 shows that there was a wide range of reading attainment.

Reading comprehension was not at this time tested; but there is no doubt that scores on a comprehension test would have been much poorer than those obtained by patients on the mechanical reading test. Moreover, scores on the Wechsler Bellevue Verbal Scale of intelligence showed rather a low correlation with those obtained on the reading test ($r = 0.43$) and some of the brightest patients were either illiterate or virtually so.

Table 28. Reading Ages of 100 Feeble-minded Adolescents tested on
Schonell's Mechanical Reading Test

Reading Age (to nearest year)	Number of Cases
14	2
13	3
12	5
11	12
10	16
9	14
8	16
7	8
6	4
5 or less	20
Total	100

For many years remedial teaching has been successfully carried out with children who are backward in reading, and current educational theory inclines to the view that even with dull children it is possible to bring reading standards up to the level of general ability as measured by intelligence tests. In recent years the army has taught large numbers of illiterate adults to read. It seemed likely that illiterate or semi-literate adolescents of dull intelligence who were resident in a mental-deficiency institution might be taught to read books and newspapers. Indeed an experimental study carried out by GUNZBURG (1948) at Monyhull colony near Birmingham had indicated that this could be done. In the investigation described here an attempt was made to study the efficacy of different methods of instruction and at the same time to investigate the effect which the incentive of being in a training workshop under good conditions of motivation would have on the acquisition of reading skill.

It was accordingly proposed to set up three workshops into which about three dozen patients would be sent. The patients were to be high-grade defectives suitable for trial on daily licence after a period of training, provided that their progress and conduct warranted it. The shops were to be "graded"—that is, there was to be a definite system of promotion from the first workshop to the second, and from the second to the third, and from the third to daily licence; and an attempt was to be made to devise criteria of promotion such that they would be comprehensible to the patients themselves. In this way, it was hoped, the time spent by the patients in the institution before they were considered suitable for licence would be broken up and the patients have comprehensible and immediate goals to work for. This, it was thought, once established, would lessen the time needed to be spent by patients in institutions before licence or discharge.

Dr. J. F. MacMAHON, Physician Superintendent of the Manor Hospital, was approached for permission to carry out this project, and a small workshop was set up in the Manor under the general supervision of our colleague Dr. F. M. Loos. An excellent supervisor, Mr. A. T. PETHICK, was appointed; and he is still in charge of the workshop. Forty-eight patients considered potentially suitable for daily licence were selected by the hospital authorities. They were young, feeble-minded men between 16 and 34 years of age. They were divided into two groups, one with I.Q.s over 70, the other with I.Q.s under 70. The ages, I.Q.s and reading ages on Schonell's tests before and after five months' instruction are given in Table 29.

The patients were matched in pairs by Matrices I.Q. and were divided by lot into two groups—an experimental group which was to be employed in the workshop, and a control group which continued their normal occupation. The teaching was carried out by Dr. J. H. CHAMPNESS, who spent a year on the staff of the Unit on a half-time basis. He tried out three methods of instruction with different groups, who were given an hour's instruction daily.

Difficulties in setting up the workshops prevented the plan from being carried out in its original form, but, modified, the experiment continued for six months. The main result of importance was the confirmation of GUNZBURG's finding that substantial improvements in literacy, as judged both by graded vocabulary and by comprehension tests, could be effected by a comparatively short period of instruction. After five months the mean improvement on the Mechanical Reading Test was one year for the patients with Matrices I.Q.s over 70 points and eight months for the lower grade group. The improvement of the higher grade patients in

Table 29.

Mechanical Reading, Spelling and Comprehension Test Results for 24 high-grade feeble-minded Men (aged 22·0 ±3·1 years, Matrices I.Q. 84·0 ±9·62 years) and 24 lower-grade feeble-minded men (aged 22·7 ± 5·6 years, Matrices I.Q. 62·2 ±5·6 years) before and after 5 months instruction

	Mechanical Reading Score (in years)	COMPREHENSION		Spelling (years)
		Timed Tests	Untimed Tests	
		(yrs. & mths.)		
High-grade Subjects				
Pre-teaching	9·5	9·2	9·5	7·5
After 5 months	10·5	10·0	12·0	9·3
Improvement	1·0	·10	2·7	1·8
Lower-grade Subjects				
Pre-teaching	6·8	8·3	8·6	6·5
After 5 months	7·6	8·4	9·10	8·2
Improvement	·8	·1	1·4	1·7

reading comprehension was 10 months for a timed test and 2 years 7 months when the students were given their own time. For lower-grade patients there was an improvement of 8 months on the mechanical reading scale. In comprehension there was practically no change on the timed test, but an improvement of 1·4 years when they were allowed their own time. (GUNZBURG in his investigation obtained results even better than these.) Dr. CHAMPNESS found that there were no significant differences between the different methods of instruction, a result that suggests that what is important in teaching backward readers is not the method used but the amount of time able to be spent with individual pupils. This, of course, is largely determined by the size of the class.

By way of comment it may be said that because of the handicaps which illiteracy or semi-literacy impose on dull adolescents who are already handicapped in other ways, there is a need for teachers and for suitable books to be placed in the libraries of mental deficiency colonies. Though there is still a shortage of suitable reading matter of interest to adult illiterates, some of the Basic English texts, which were extensively used by Dr. CHAMPNESS, appear very suitable for teaching educationally subnormal adults. Again, since reading can be taught so easily, further research is needed to determine why, after ten years of schooling, young people should still be unable to read, or alternatively, why they forget so quickly what they have learnt at school. The need for further research is closely connected with the need for providing more adequate opportunities for those who have failed to progress at school, and for an adequate and properly qualified teaching staff in mental-deficiency hospitals.

3. *The Third Investigation—Experimental Studies of Motivation and Performance*

To throw light on some of the factors which influence training and performance several investigations have been carried out with imbeciles. Imbeciles, rather than high-grade defectives, have been used in these experiments for a number of reasons:

(*a*) Though there are large numbers of imbeciles in the community little research has been done on them and it is important to know what are the potentialities and abilities of these severely handicapped persons.

(*b*) Imbeciles are probably less immediately influenced by social determinants, long-term goals and other factors arising from social life in a large hospital than are the feeble-minded patients.

(*c*) Since large numbers of them are to be found in wards and hospital workshops where they do little work, they are readily available as subjects for experiments.

(*d*) It seemed possible that imbeciles might under suitable conditions be taught to do useful and constructive work in circumstances which would promote their own development.

Though because of qualitative differences there are many respects in which it may not be possible to generalize from imbeciles to the feeble-minded, their conduct is governed by many of the same principles, and it is a matter for investigation to determine to what extent findings obtained with imbeciles can be generalized to higher-grade patients and to human behaviour in general.

The work done has been of two sorts: (i) a number of laboratory investigations were carried out mainly by Dr. GORDON (1954, 1955); (ii) Workshop investigations were carried out by Dr. LOOS (1955). A brief account will be given of these studies and of later work reported by other investigators.

Dr. GORDON studied incentives. In his first series of experiments he used an endurance test. This test—the "leg persistence test"— requires a subject to sit on a kitchen chair with his arms by his sides and to hold one leg out horizontally above another chair of the same height for as long as he can. The test has hitherto been used to compare groups of neurotics and healthy controls on "persistence", lack of which is believed to characterise neurotics. We used the test for a different purpose—namely, as a simple and objectively scorable task on which to assess the effects of different conditions of motivation upon performance. The study was in some ways similar to investigations carried out by MACKWORTH (1950) on the performance of naval recruits on tasks involving heavy manual labour to the point of exhaustion under different conditions of humidity, temperature and motivation.

In the first experiment 27 imbeciles aged between 16 and 30 were used as subjects. Their I.Q.s on the 1937 Revision of the Stanford Binet test were between 23 and 49 points. All were clinically classified as imbeciles and there was no reason to doubt the correctness of any of the diagnoses. The patients were each given the test on two successive days. They were ranked according to their performance and divided by lot into three matched groups. They were then individually given the test once a day for 10 days, the members of each group working under a different condition of motivation. One group, in which the subjects took the test under standard laboratory conditions and without comment by the examiner, served as a control group. Those in the second group were constantly encouraged to do their best throughout their performance, while the members of the third group were given targets to beat which were based on their previous best performance on the test. These targets or *Goals* were presented graphically; they consisted of a piece of cardboard graduated up the sides like a mercury thermometer, up which a pointer was pulled by a piece of string. The previous best performance was marked by a paper clip.

The mean score of each group on each day of the first ten days is shown graphically in Fig. 1.

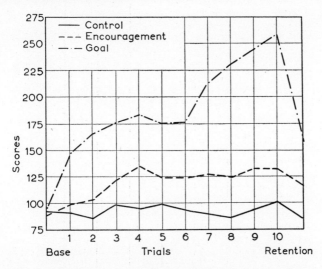

FIG. 1. Leg Persistence: mean score for trials 1–10, and retention for Control, Encouragement and Goal groups.

From Fig. 1 it is clear that incentives had an enormous effect, greatly increasing the performance of members in the two groups which were given special incentives. The average time which members of the Encouragement group continued at the test on the 10th day was 132 seconds, while the Goal group averaged 258 seconds. In contrast the Control group fluctuated between 86 and 101 seconds during the 10-day period, a performance typical of that obtained from normal subjects when they do this test without special incentives.

Though numbers in the groups were small they were again subdivided at the end of the 10th day. Half of the Control group and half of the Encouragement group (the 2nd, 4th, 6th and 8th in order of excellence of performance) were put under Goal conditions. Half of the Goal group were put under Encouragement.

The experiment was continued for a further 10 days. The graph of performance is shown in Fig. 2 which includes also the scores represented in Fig. 1.

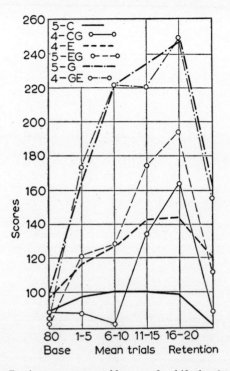

FIG. 2. Leg Persistence: mean weekly scores for shifted and non-shifted groups.

It can be seen that under the superior motivating conditions of Goal, performance increased markedly. But there were significant differences between the performance of groups under the same objective conditions. The group which had worked under Goal conditions from the start had the highest scores; those who began under Encouragement conditions came next, and those who changed from Control conditions came next, those in the Control group showing little improvement during their subsequent trials. The remaining group which changed from Goal conditions to Encouragement continued to improve, and in fact their performance did not differ significantly from that of those who remained under Goal conditions.

Groups changed to the superior motivating condition (Goal) showed that performance was a function not only of the objective conditions under which the task was done, and the physical strength of the patients who did it, but also of the past history of the subjects. Inferior conditions during the earlier stages of the experiment depressed performance at later stages, even when conditions were improved. At the same time, however, the improvement in conditions resulted in marked improvement in performance. Whether or not a deterioration in conditions leads to a comparable decrease in performance is a matter for further investigation. The fact that the Goal group when changed to Encouragement continued to increase in performance suggests that it does not, but the evidence is not adequate to enable firm conclusions to be drawn.

One month after the completion of the experiment the test was given again. The results of the six groups are also shown graphically in Fig. 2.

A curious feature of these results was that performance on retest was found to be more influenced by the conditions under which the test was taken during the *first* ten days than by the equally long, and more recent experience of the following ten days in which the changed motivating conditions were operating. Numbers in the groups are perhaps too small to enable firm conclusions to be drawn from this finding; if it were confirmed in later experiments using larger numbers and different tasks it might have an important bearing on the treatment of imbeciles, and on learning theory in psychology.

GORDON then carried out a series of experiments with imbeciles using a laboratory task which could be continued indefinitely. The task was to place one-inch nails one at a time into the holes of a wire mesh frame, working down each column before beginning the next. Larger groups of subjects were used, four matched groups with ten subjects in each carrying out the experiment under four conditions of motivation—Control and Goal conditions and two types of competition. The results of this experiment confirmed, though in less striking fashion, the findings obtained in the persistence test.

GORDON's work has been continued by CLARIDGE (O'CONNOR

and CLARIDGE, 1954), using the continuous laboratory task. The same subjects as had been tested by GORDON were retested on the task after an interval of a year. During the first two days of CLARIDGE's experiment the subjects were tested in the groups to which they had been originally allotted by GORDON. (All 40 of GORDON's subjects were still available.) At the beginning of the first trial the procedure to be followed was briefly outlined, but, CLARIDGE reports, this was found to be unnecessary, as all subjects remembered what to do. They were given the test to do for an hour under control conditions, and from the first all settled down quickly.

The results showed that the level of performance achieved on retest was equal to about the performance level reached on the 30th trial of GORDON's experiment, which lasted for 42 trials. The Goal group retained its superiority upon retest, the Control group being significantly inferior. The others were intermediate.

CLARIDGE's later work was concerned with the factors affecting goal-striving. He showed the importance of combining goal-striving with encouragement—targets to aim at were not very effective incentives unless "success" had some social significance (in this case given by the experimenter encouraging the subjects and sympathizing with those who failed to reach their targets). A somewhat similar finding had previously been made in workshop studies which are reported below. CLARIDGE observes that the results indicate the importance of social approval as an incentive; secondly, the "consistent retention shown over a period of one year since GORDON's earlier work provides somewhat unusual evidence of the relatively long-term effects of an external incentive. Such a finding may have implications similar to HEBB's (1952) experiments, and may demonstrate the importance of good incentive conditions in early stages of training."

More recently further studies have been carried out by WALTON and BEGG (1955) using the leg persistence test. They also note the importance of social approval as a factor in the improvement of the performance of imbeciles, and add that performance deteriorates if the task is sufficiently tedious and devoid of interest. Deterioration takes place much earlier if little or no attention is paid to the imbecile.

WALTON and BEGG sum up the findings of the various laboratory studies (and of workshop studies described in the next section) as follows:

"It appears . . . that defectives do respond in an essentially normal way to incentives. Contrary to usual clinical opinion it appears also wrong to assume that defectives, because of low intelligence, can be left to do simple, uninspiring tasks similar to those suggested by Tredgold and Lewis, for we have seen that under similar conditions to these they lose interest and their performance deteriorates.

". . . Not only will our views on the supervision and training of mental defectives have to be reconsidered but 'face-value' impressions of the abilities of defectives will need to give rise to carefully controlled experiments to determine how best their abilities can be employed to the advantage both of the subjects themselves and of the community."

4. *The Fourth Investigation—Workshop Studies with Imbeciles*

An attempt was made to apply GORDON'S techniques to stimulate the production of imbeciles working in a hospital workshop. We wished to find out (1) whether young adult imbeciles of medium grade who were not psychotic or seriously disturbed or crippled could be taught to do a simple industrial job with sufficient care and skill to justify their employment on it; (2) what incentives would enable them to work consistently and happily throughout a normal working day without compulsion or punishment.

Six imbecile youths were selected and brought into the workshop in which at that time only high-grade patients were employed. The imbeciles were taken from the hospital brush shop and were selected by the supervisor as being among the least competent of the patients under 30 years of age in the shop. Their ages and I.Q.s on the 1937 Terman Merrill Revision of the Stanford Binet Scale were:

Subject No.:	1	2	3	4	5	6
Age:	19	20	18	20	23	23
I.Q.:	42	41	22	34	37	33

The patients have since been described by CLARKE and HERMELIN (1955) as follows:

"The group includes one mongol and one congenital syphilitic; the condition of another may have resulted from spinal meningitis at the age of 3; another is of syphilitic stock; another had scarlet fever at an early age which may have been a relevant factor; and in the final case the aetiology is obscure.

"Two of the six look fairly normal, while the remaining four look typically imbecile; two can hardly talk at all, although the remainder are quite garrulous. Three cannot name colours correctly, but all can match them; two are hoarders of rubbish and two are unstable, one of the latter showing apparently psychotic traits. Four of the six do not know their ages, a 24-year-old saying that he is aged 10, while another of the same age merely maintains that he is 'over 18'. Only one can count above ten, and two cannot really count at all. Thus in all respects these are typical imbeciles; and their response to psychological tests of any sort is exceedingly poor."

The patients were trained by Dr. LOOS to fold boxes. An efficient method of folding was taught which involved making nine specific movements with both hands and in the correct order. Correct movements were insisted on from the first and all mistakes had to be corrected as soon as they were made or discovered by the investigator. The training took two weeks.

Immediately after the training was completed the subjects worked continuously each day on box folding, for a period of five weeks. Records of output for each boy were kept. Although production fluctuated considerably all patients were able to do the job, and at the end of eleven weeks in the shop in which they spent their whole time on this job their mean folding time was actually faster than that of the best high-grade patients. The results of tests in which both groups were timed while folding ten boxes as quickly as possible on two different occasions are given in Table 30. This shows that in their ability to do the job the imbecile groups were soon as good as the feeble-minded group.

The imbeciles did not, however, work as consistently as did the higher-grade patients and their daily production was much below their potential. It was clear that a more difficult task than that of

Table 30. Box Folding Times of Imbeciles and Moron Subjects

	Imbeciles	Morons
Mean I.Q.	33	71
Range of I.Q.s	24–41	55–96
Mean time in seconds to fold a box		
(a) one week after imbeciles began work	17·1	—
(b) 11 weeks after imbeciles began work	8·8	10·8
Number of cases	6	6

teaching them a skill was to teach them to exercise it. We therefore turned to problems of motivation, and two experiments were carried out to test the effect of different motive-incentive conditions on production.

First Experiment

The conditions examined in the first of these experiments were patterned after ones which had been used by GORDON. To demonstrate to the subjects how their output in box folding compared with that of previous days, histograms were constructed on squared paper. Each boy's daily production was shown in column form. Boxes were issued in bundles of approximately 150. As each bundle was finished, a square was filled in for that day, and the patient was given a new bundle. In this way it was possible to give the subjects a visual picture of how much had been done already during the day, and how much had still to be done if they were to beat their previous or any other day's total output.

The increase in weekly production which resulted from giving the subjects daily goals is shown in Fig. 3 (weeks 2–6).

The results obtained confirm GORDON's finding that when given goals to work for, imbeciles are capable of sustained response over a considerable period of time. They contradict his results, obtained both with the leg persistence test and in his subsequent study, in that whereas he found a continuous rise in output we found an initial rise followed by a gradual fall. It should be noted that GORDON found no falling off in output either in groups given self-competition or subjected to other incentive conditions. Differences arose only in the ultimate level of performance achieved by the

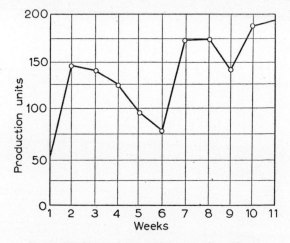

FIG. 3. Weekly production of six imbecile subjects.
Week 1 is base; weeks 2 to 6—Experiment 1; weeks 7 to 11—
Experiment 2. (See text.)

groups, those being given goals or self-competition achieving better results than those given encouragement, group competition, or individual competition.

The later work of CLARIDGE and of WALTON and BEGG on the importance of social approval as an incentive clears up the apparent discrepancy between LOOS's findings and GORDON's. At the time we suspected that the difference might lie in the different experimental conditions prevailing in the two experiments and that the experimental conditions themselves might determine the results obtained. An attempt was therefore made to change the structure of the workshop by having the imbeciles no longer work in another room, isolated from the rest of the shop, but integrated in the work of the total unit of which they were a part.

Second Experiment

The workshops were rearranged so that the folders and gluers worked as members of common teams. Under the new conditions, instead of the folders pooling their work and the gluers taking their boxes from the pool, each feeble-minded patient employed on gluing was assigned to work with an imbecile who was to do all his folding. Small working units were thus formed. If the folders got behind in their work the gluers were unable to continue with theirs.

The experiment lasted five weeks, at the end of which a reorganization of the workshop made it impossible to continue. The weekly output figures for the group of imbeciles are shown in Fig. 3 (weeks 7–11). They can be compared with the figures for the previous study which are also shown in Fig. 3 (weeks 2–6), and which have already been discussed.

The second experiment followed immediately after the conclusion of the first. In the new situation production showed an immediate rise, and during the five weeks the experiment lasted there was no indication that the level of production would fall off. Only during one week (week 9 in Fig. 3 and the third week of this particular experiment) did production fall. This was brought about through a hold-up in the gluing process.

Not only did weekly production increase, but the efficiency of the patients, using criteria specially designed to measure this, also increased. Using an efficiency ratio which had been employed before the first experiment began (the ratio of average daily production to peak production in five minute speed trials), it was found that the imbeciles now worked at an average of 66 per cent of their new peak production figures as against 44 per cent during the first experiment.

From a technical point of view this last experiment is weak. It was not possible to use control groups and so to run the experiments concurrently, or to balance the order in which the studies were carried out. It cannot definitely be stated therefore that the results obtained were not due to learning or practice, though the evidence is against such an explanation. Nor was it possible to keep the same teams working together throughout the experimental period, owing to sickness and absence among the high-grade patients. Hence it is possible that it was the continuing novelty of the situation which brought about the change. An argument against this is that one team remained intact throughout the experiment and achieved results comparable with those obtained by the other groups. Again, there was a change in the type of

I

supervision the patients were given when they were placed in the same room as the higher-grade patients and this in itself may have affected them.

These and other factors might possibly have accounted for some or even all of the changes observed. It seems most likely, however, that the main factor responsible for the change was the alteration in the structure of the workshop. The imbeciles, instead of working only with other patients of the same grade, now found themselves co-operating with high-grade patients on terms of equality, making a manifestly important contribution to the total job. For perhaps the first time in their lives they were able actually to see that what they were doing was useful and to understand how it was related to a finished product. Even the patients with Binet I.Q.s in the 20's developed a sense of pride in the work of "their team".

The restructuring of the workshop had an unexpected effect on the high-grade patients working in the training workshop. Their output in some cases also rose considerably and their efficiency as workers increased. The division of the patients into small groups might thus be thought to have made it possible for them to develop an enhanced sense of their own individuality; it increased their sense of personal responsibility for their actions and brought about improvements both in output and in conduct. MARRIOTT (1949) has noted that among normal workers there is also a correlation between output and the smallness of the working group, though the association is not so large as was observed with the defectives. Further investigation of this problem is desirable.

The later history of these patients is not without interest. CLARKE and HERMELIN (1955) give the following description:

> "For the last two and a half years these 6 imbeciles have been employed as cardboard-box-folders in a small experimental workshop, where their work and behaviour have been carefully observed. On the average, their output of cardboard boxes has been 30,000–40,000 per thirty-five-hour week, but on occasion—e.g., when a special order had to be fulfilled rapidly—they have reached 60,000–70,000. During the whole of this period sickness has been very rare; most have had feverish colds or influenza, but there has been nothing more serious. Supervision is minimal, since they work reliably and

consistently; in fact, the supervisor normally is at the other end of the building and merely visits this workshop every hour or so—a fact of importance in view of traditional attitudes about the necessity of continuous supervision. Indeed one weekend, in the absence of the supervisor, all 6 imbeciles became bored, gained access to the closed workshop, and worked all morning without any supervision at all. For the last two years it has been clear that they can do a full day's work reliably and well, earning money thereby; and, further, they have every appearance of enjoying their more active life."

Later Studies

Workshop investigations carried out by CLARKE and HERMELIN since the conclusion of our studies have gone well beyond the rather tentative efforts we made to investigate the employability of imbeciles. The same 6 subjects have taken part in these later studies. In these experiments imbeciles were trained to do industrial assembly jobs of considerable complexity—to use a simple guillotine to cut insulated wire to exact lengths; to use a soldering iron to solder four different coloured wires to the correct terminals of an 8-pin television plug; and to assemble a bicycle-pump, adding the screws and washers in their correct order in a sequence of 9 operations.

CLARKE and HERMELIN'S paper is a landmark in the history of research on the trainability of imbeciles; it shows more clearly than our study some of the untouched possibilities for research with, and practical training of, imbeciles. Four of their conclusions may be mentioned:

(1) The initial ability of imbeciles on industrial as on other tasks tends to be exceedingly low.

(2) Their initial ability has little relationship with the level achieved with training.

(3) The main distinction between the performance of imbeciles and others on simple tasks is not so much the end-level as the time taken to achieve it.

(4) The qualities such as manual dexterity and motor co-ordination are not static, but are capable of improvement within limits which are often ill understood and ill defined.

CHAPTER EIGHT

OCCUPATIONAL ADAPTATION IN THE COMMUNITY

FOLLOWING the establishment of the workshop, and during investigations carried on there, patients were sent out to work in the community during the day, and returned to the hospital at night. Their success or failure at work, especially at a building site, at which about 60 were employed, constitutes the subject matter of this chapter.

The present chapter considers the relative success of defectives working in the community on jobs normally allotted to people who have never been certified. The fact that feeble-mindedness is, to some degree, a character or personality problem was stated as a probability. Other evidence in this connection might have been culled from numerous recent sources such as BURT (1937) and PENROSE (1938). Having established, through our investigations, that the I.Q. of the feeble-minded is unlikely to have a mean much below 70 points,* and having shown that large numbers of them are free from disabling neuroses, at least as measured psychometrically, we expected that considerable success would result from their employment in industry if this could be accomplished. Fortunately, at the time at which the investigations reported in previous chapters were being carried out, Darenth Park was engaged on a programme of expanding licence for the feeble-minded which increased the percentage of available feeble-minded males on day work between April 1949 and March 1951 from 11 per cent to 27 per cent (approx.). The Unit was able to test and study many of these patients and to see them on the job either on a building site near the hospital or at a factory making plastics. The performance and success of these boys is sufficiently impressive to report in some detail.

Male patients numbering more than 50 were employed on the

---

* WEINER has shown (1955) that the figure of 70 points is a very close approximation to the mean I.Q. of defectives under statutory supervision, just as previous work reported above showed it to be characteristic of institutional patients.

building site at St. Paul's Cray in Kent, and about 30 at a factory.
Others were employed on municipal gardens and farms and in
private houses. Most of these other locations did not offer such
facilities for study of work conditions as did the two first and it is
with these two that we are primarily concerned. Both groups were
given fairly continuous work from April 1949 in one case for about
18 months, and in the other for about one year terminating at the
same time. During this time, of course, individuals changed and
moved from one job to the other or out to long licence, or were
withdrawn from work for some misdemeanour. Each personal
difficulty was dealt with in one case by a nurse specially located on
the building site, and in the other by the foreman of the shop in
which the patients worked, who was a man of considerable insight
into the problems the lads had to face.

As any patient's defection from his job for whatever reason was
noted in a hospital licence book, it was possible to obtain records of
the patients who worked on the jobs and to get out certain norms of
behaviour. This was done on a comparative basis for the building
site and in a more limited way for the factory. The figures for
success in the factory were given in Chapter 6 and only the building site experience will be described here.

Success and Failure at the Building Site

When the success of boys on this site was estimated, the following conclusions were drawn. Among the 60 to 70 boys employed on
the site for a period of 18 months, dismissals followed a definite
pattern. At first there was a great deal of maladjustment due
apparently to the poor physique of some of the patients. As compared with normal labourers, the percentage failures were at least
half again as large during the first month. However, this period of
adjustment and trial over, failures dropped to half the normal level
during the remainder of the quarter. During the second quarter,
which was early summer, failure on both normal controls and the
defective patients fell off, but the defective failure rate was still half
the normal rate. During the second half of the year failures among
the defectives increased and were again double those of the normal
workers. Finally, stability was reached during the second year and
a failure rate of two-thirds that of normal workers was established.

The second failure period for the defectives corresponded with the development of a sense of new-won independence and represented a revolt against what they considered the over-strict discipline to which they were subjected in the hospital. They made unfavourable comparisons between their liberties and those of the normal workers.

Reasons for initial failure were investigated in detail and appeared for the most part to be due to the wrong job being allotted to a boy. Other causes have been supposed to be the failure to allow a boy time to settle down in his job. Apparently many young patients require about a month to become accustomed to a job, and if they are sacked for failing to do good work before this period has run out they have no opportunity of showing their powers. Laziness or failure to do adequate work was very seldom mentioned as a cause of dismissal and cases of insubordination were few. We are forced to infer that physical incapacity and lack of time to settle down are two of the chief causes for adolescent patients failing at this kind of work. Thirdly, it is obvious that many patients take their anti-social reaction or neurotic difficulties to work with them, and their output and work behaviour reflect these difficulties. In a list of unsatisfactory boys who were eventually regarded as complete failures, half were thought to be neurotic or delinquent on the basis of some psychological tests and also on the basis of their behaviour record. Of an equal number of successes, few had been found disturbed. On the other hand, some who do not fail are also noted for their bad behaviour or neurotic tendency in hospital, and half the failures were not emotionally unstable.

The evidence of the overall successes of the boys employed at this site shows that their failure rates are not greater than but less than those of day-labourers who undertake such work. At the same time it must be made clear that day-labourers suffer fewer consequences if they leave work, and are not subject to detention and other punishments in this event.

Table 31. *Percentage "Failures" on Building Site*

Failures	1st month	2nd and 3rd month	4th to 6th month	7th to 12th month	Still employed after 1 year
Defectives	34%	12%	7%	27%	20%
Controls	21%	24%	13%	13%	29%

217 stoppages were recorded with 134 different defectives who were working at St. Paul's Cray for 18 months; that is, 1·4 stoppages per person or 0·08 stoppages per person per month. Of these:

	57 per cent were due to sickness
	12 per cent were due to poor physique
and	7 per cent were due to redundancy or discharge to long licence

Total   76 per cent

The remainder may be considered failures for more serious or less easily avoidable reasons:

	5 per cent absented from the hospital
	2 per cent suffered accidents
	3 per cent discharged themselves
and	14 per cent were discharged for indiscipline

Total   24 per cent

The breakdown of failures by months is of some interest. 151 cases of stoppage after one month were recorded. Over 43 per cent of these were due to "sickness", and were mostly temporary. Of first month stoppages apart from these, the major classes were due to poor physique, transfers or discharges mostly for disciplinary reasons and disagreements. Each of these represented just under 16 per cent of all first month stoppages, and with sickness therefore, account for 91 per cent of such stoppages. Escapes and discharges at own request account for most of the rest.

Discharges after one month's work account for just under 70 per cent of all stoppages, and of these over 50 per cent were first months of work for the person concerned. 65 per cent in all were stoppages occurring in successive one-month intervals. Second- and third-month stoppages represent 17 per cent of all stoppages and were overwhelmingly due to sickness (73 per cent). Escapes represent 5 per cent during this period as compared with 4 per cent in the first month.

In the second quarter of the working period, stoppages were only 11 per cent of all stoppages. In the remaining 9 months stoppages were only 2 per cent of all stoppages. Sickness again accounts for most. Patients who remain on the job longer than six months show no stoppages other than those due to holidays or transfers. This is also virtually true of those who stay more than three months.

If one considers that most sickness was of a temporary nature and that transfers account for many other stoppages and may be set aside for our purposes, the number of stoppages which might appear to be due to psychological causes can be much reduced. Using this revised figure 72 stoppages occurred and of these exactly one third were due to poor physique. Slightly more than one third were attributed to inter-personal difficulties and 12 per cent to patients absconding. Thus the record of these patients on many accounts is equal to, if not better than, that usually obtained with building workers. These successes are striking examples of what those of low intelligence can achieve at unskilled work.

It should be pointed out, of course, that the patients whose records appear here in statistical form represent a very diverse group with many different problems. In some cases the fact that the more unstable of them were supported by the hospital to which they could retreat was the possible cause of their ultimate success in staying a long time at the work after one or two failures. In other cases, on the other hand, the fact that they had no alternative employment such as was available to the normal workers, may have made their behaviour more tractable and discipline more effective. However, these reservations only slightly reduce the generality of the conclusion that feeble-minded patients at present confined to hospitals might easily contribute valuable work to industry or public works if administrative arrangements could be made for them to work under normal conditions. A strong point should also be made of the fact that a building site can scarcely be called sheltered. Possibly the worst kind of supervision exists and conditions of work are hard. Most of the fellow-workers a patient may meet will not be in a position to help him or advise him if a problem arises. Many workers have financial, personal or social problems with which they do not well know how to cope, and so are not good advisers.

The successes achieved by people at this level are matched by the average work success of boys leaving school in some districts whom intelligence testing has shown to be of the same level of I.Q. as those certified patients described in this section. It is therefore of interest to consider the case of these boys, on average 2 years younger than the patients, but in intellectual level, equivalent.

A Study of Boys of Subnormal Intelligence

The success of the feeble-minded patients employed on the St. Paul's Cray building site, is one example of the possibility of employing patients whose I.Q. is between imbecile and normal level, in most cases. Results of a similar kind reinforcing the conclusion of the St. Paul's Cray survey were obtained when the work success of 47 subnormal boys was compared with that of 47 boys of normal I.Q. in Derby. These boys were chosen on the basis of their 11-plus selection intelligence test scores and were divided into two groups for low and normal I.Q. and paired with each other according to class and school. In this way a representative sample of school-leavers from all the Secondary Modern schools in Derby was obtained. The mean I.Q. of the lower-intelligence group, the experimental group, was 70 points with a range from 65 to 80 points. The mean I.Q. of the higher-intelligence group, the control group, was 99·5 points with a range from 94 points to 106 points of I.Q. Despite the mean difference of 30 points of I.Q. the resulting difference in the work record of the two groups of boys was small. The subnormal boys had had an average of 2·8 jobs in the two years between leaving school and joining the army and the normal boys had had an average of 1·5 jobs. Although the difference is significant at the 5-per-cent level, the work success and behaviour of the subnormal group as rated by employers was not significantly different from the ratings accorded to the normal group. The difference seemed to be due to the number of subnormal boys who left apprenticed trades in which they had begun; 12 out of 21 of the subnormal left such positions as compared with five out of 29 of the normal boys.

Summarizing briefly, the boys of subnormal intelligence in this study were enabled to fulfil a useful role as working citizens in all cases, even though the need for guidance along lines different from those offered to normals is indicated by a slightly higher failure rate. The difference in success of the two groups is partly explained by the failure of the backward boys in skilled trade training. This bears out other findings of a similar kind referred to in a previous chapter. It is also partly explained by the greater reaction of backward boys to loss of parents and the slightly greater family size among this group. The great success of boys of a mean I.Q. 30 points below normal reinforces the general argument presented here, namely that in certain economic and social conditions, lack of intelligence is not a serious handicap in unskilled work. It is especially important to observe that the mean I.Q. of the backward boys was identical with that of the feeble-minded boys tested in a hospital for defectives.

Many examples of success at work could be quoted from other authors. CHARLES'S (1953) and BALLER'S classic study (1936) provide two. Such studies show that at least two-thirds and probably four-fifths of those who might on I.Q. score be classed as feeble-minded, can live in financial and social independence under present economic circumstances.

CHAPTER NINE

PSYCHOTHERAPY WITH UNSTABLE DEFECTIVES*

IN CHAPTERS 4 and 5 the existence of a group of neurotic feeble-minded adolescents numbering perhaps as much as 12 per cent of all the male feeble-minded patients in hospital was referred to. Some of the characteristics of these neurotics were mentioned. It was suggested that this group was handicapped in human relations and at work by inadequate persistence and general instability. Unlike many other unstable patients in the hospital, they could not be persuaded to make an obvious change in their behaviour by being first trained in the experimental workshops and then given an opportunity of working at some job in the community. Frequently they broke down because of some act of indiscipline or because of some unkindness which the other defectives would have complained about and forgotten but which affected them more deeply. This group cannot be ignored because it represents a minority, and although the task of tracing the cause of their disturbance is unlikely to be an easy one, it must be attempted.

The characteristic response of a busy nurse in charge of this kind of patient is to impose an impartial, kindly but strict discipline which, although sympathetic in many respects, is of necessity limited by shortage of time and the large number of patients whom he is expected to supervise. While adequate for stable patients, such discipline takes no account of the anti-authoritarian and anti-social attitude so characteristic of many of these delinquent adolescents. The punishments sometimes imposed justly and without bitterness only have the effect of confirming the patient in his anti-social prejudices. Some further analysis of the probable causes of the attitudes characteristic of these patients is needed. Very little evidence on the success of any treatment with this kind of defective is available in the psychological literature.

---

* The work reported in this chapter was carried out in collaboration with Dr. K. YONGE.

The Problem

Group treatment has been shown to be effective as a treatment in the case of certain patients. Essentially it consists of more or less directed discussion between a psychiatrist and a group of patients. It is usually thought that such treatment is likely to be effective chiefly where patients are relatively intelligent.

The evidence against group treatment of unstable defectives may be summarized as follows. HEALY and BRONNER (1936) found a relationship between intelligence and the outcome of therapy. Specifically for group treatment, WENDER (1936) decided from his work that intellectual impairment prevents success with group treatment. COTZIN (1948) and PATTERSON (1950), working with boys and girls respectively, reached the conclusion that the subnormal had no benefit from therapy. FOULKES (1948) states that the ability to express ideas clearly in words is essential to therapeutic success. BROMBERG (1948) takes an identical view.

On the other side of the discussion, SARASON (1949) and GLASSMAN (1942-43) seem to be the two notable exceptions to those who have found group psychotherapy a failure with the backward. Even these have limited their claims to the upper ranks of backwardness, namely the dull or those above I.Q. 75.

Theoretical objections to the use of group discussion with defectives and psychopaths come from HENDERSON and GILLESPIE (1950) and SLAVSON (1947), who believe that the part played in a group by psychopaths is different from the part played by other sorts of patients. FRIEDLANDER (1947) also summarizes the views of other investigators as indicating the constitutional basis of psychopathic character. She herself is optimistic, as is GLOVER (1944) about the use of group techniques. But on the whole the mass of psychiatric opinion appears to be that prognosis in cases where

Table 32. Estimated Relationship of Group Treatment Failure and Intelligence

I.Q. range	Percentage of treatment failures
Above 110	10
80-89	23
70-79	66

psychopathy and mental deficiency are combined is very poor indeed. HEALY and BRONNER (1936) state the view of many. They give the preceding table on figures for delinquents. They conclude "counselling or psychotherapy do not seem applicable to mental defectives".

The Investigation

Twenty-one highly unstable or psychopathic adolescent defectives were carefully selected from a larger group pre-selected by one of the hospital psychiatrists. All were recent admissions who had failed to adjust to occupational work within the institution and had been subjected to various forms of discipline. All were considered severe behaviour problems. None was physically defective.

This group was divided into three groups matched for I.Q.s and age. Mean ages of the boys in each of the sub-groups was 18, 19 and 20 respectively. All were between 15 and 22. The mean Matrices I.Q.s of the groups were 81, 83 and 77 respectively. On the Wechsler Verbal Scale means were even closer, being 64, 69 and 67. There were no significant differences between the groups on either of these two variables. Matching for type of behaviour disorder was not so easy and could not be certainly checked but every effort was made to achieve equivalence. Thus the psychiatrist rejected many cases of equal severity in seeking sets of 3 patients with similar symptomatology. The extent to which this was successful was largely the extent to which the first group of 21 cases was a homogeneous group whose history showed an inability to profit from experience and a tendency to repeat anti-social behaviour.

Each of the groups thus formed was assigned at random to one of three routines, ordinary hospital care (*control*), special workshop training without therapy (*workshop control*), and special workshop training plus group treatment (*experimental*). The control group apart, the other two groups could be compared at work for output and behaviour as well as before and after treatment. The control group at the disposal of the hospital authorities was not always a control group in every sense because the hospital was unable to retain them within the walls for the experimental period. This meant that they were subject to different conditions.

As both the other two groups worked in the same workshop and both were supervised by the same person, being separated only by a screen wall, they were in a position to be watched and their work and general behaviour checked and compared on identical scales. This was done. In addition, one group was given two one-hour treatment sessions per week in a separate room. During this period the psychiatrist observed them and afterwards rated their behaviour, but in addition their conversation was recorded on a tape recorder and they were watched by an unseen investigator who checked their behaviour on a check list as well as afterwards rating them on the same scales as were used by the psychiatrist. All groups were given tests of intelligence and neurotic tendency before and after the period of treatment.

Treatment

Treatment is perhaps an inexact term for the non-directive discussion which took place 32 times in a period of six months with the experimental group of 7 boys. However, the changes which took place in the members of the experimental group were measurable and, in view of the circumstances, impressive. These results were achieved in the face of original opposition on the part of the patients who regarded the first sessions solely as an excuse to escape from routine. Despite this lack of interest and unawareness of their own problems, the psychiatrist refrained from direction of any sort and simply presented himself in the role of a sympathetic listener who did not identify himself either with the patients or with the hospital authorities, but who allowed the expression of a good number of anti-authoritarian statements during the earlier sessions without comment or apparent disapproval.

Discussion was extensive, and, with one or two minor halts, continuous throughout the treatment. As the psychiatrist had made it clear that he wanted to hear anything of interest to the boys, he placed no restriction on topics of conversation which frequently centred around cheap literature of sex or violence, or the shortcomings of the staff or the institution. Conversations were often explosive and accompanying activities sometimes anti-social or destructive. The psychiatrist tried to restrain more extreme expressions of feeling without appearing to side with authority.

Recorded Results

The effects of the treatment may be assessed in a number of
ways, according to improvement in diligence in the workshop, to
improvement in workshop behaviour as rated by observers, or
according to the changes in the treatment group as shown in
verbalization or behaviour during treatment sessions. Effects might
also show themselves in pre- and post-testing differences. Each of
these is discussed briefly in the succeeding sections, but in summary it can be said that attitudes among treated patients changed
significantly in certain respects, namely, in a decrease in sadistic
expressions, negative attitudes to authority and with increases in
intra-group criticism, zest and ambition. These were defined as
clear statements expressing one or other of the attitudes. Changes
in diligence were also noted, increases being significant statistically. Behaviour was notably improved. Tests showed no changes
in neurotic tendency, but a rise in verbal intelligence significant at
the 5-per-cent level was recorded. The change was 9 points and no
equivalent change was recorded in the other two control groups.
No change in neurotic tendency was recorded on any one of
several objective tests, including persistence and body sway
suggestibility.

Time Sampling of Work Behaviour

Throughout the period of the treatment, both the experimental
and control groups working side by side in nearby shops carried
out the same tasks. Observers noted their behaviour four times a
day by making a time sample of whether or not they were working
throughout the ten seconds of the sample, not working at all or
working half the time. Independent checks on the reliability of the
technique were made, and high percentage agreements between
observers were found, all above 90 per cent. The supervisor of the
shop made a weekly estimate of the behaviour of each boy on a
check list. Both measures showed that significant gains took place
in the treatment group, although no change could be detected in
the workshop control group. In the case of diligence as measured
by time sampling of work carried out in the workshop, the difference between the first and last 10 measures when finally tested by
't' test was found to be significant as the 2-per-cent level. The

behaviour check list change measured between the first half of the period and the second half was significant at the 5-per-cent level.

Changes in the Treatment Group

Changes measurable in terms of verbal expression or other expressive behaviour during the treatment sessions were recorded at the time, either by the observer using a check list or by the tape recording of conversation. In addition both experimenters took account of each patient's behaviour in each session and ranked them immediately afterwards on a scale of participation or monopolization of the discussion. The rating was done independently and was called a Dominance Scale. Its reliability or inter-rater consistency proved to be good, yielding a rank order correlation of 0·96.

Recorded conversations were analysed for expressions of attitudes and the number of aggressive, sadistic, critical or negative expressions noted. The changes noted throughout the treatment are recorded together with their direction and significance levels in Table 33. A check on the reliability of the analysis of the spoken record was made by having another observer, the psychologist, work through a random selection of recorded sessions and count the different expressions, allotting them to their appropriate classification. The results of the two analyses were then compared in these cases. Percentage agreements were calculated, and were found to lie between 82 and 100 per cent.

One point is important from a therapeutic point of view. Previously it was made clear that dominance in conversation was reliably estimated by ranking. In addition, continuous observation by the psychologist, using a check list of behaviour items during treatment sessions, enabled a further check of the rank orders agreed by the psychologist and psychiatrist on the basis of their impressions. The finally agreed figure, the sum of interjections counted during each session, was found to be related to verbal I.Q. as measured by tests made before treatment started.

Of the two boys who improved most as a result of treatment, one had poor vocalization and low verbal intelligence, while the other had high dominance and high verbal intelligence. The findings therefore suggested that neither of the two related variables of vocalization or verbal I.Q. is related to benefit derived from treatment. This agrees well with KRAUPL-TAYLOR's findings (personal communication). Results comparing the verbal attitudes of the two groups during treatment are given in Table 33.

Table 33. Significance of Changes in Attitudes Recorded During Group Therapy

	Direction of Change	"t"	Level of Significance
Appreciation. Zest	Increase	4·093	·001
Sadism. Masochism	Decrease	4·911	·001
Negative attitude to group members	Increase	3·980	·01
Positive attitude to authority figures	Increase	2·750	·02
Fanciful ambitions	Increase	2·643	·02
Real ambitions	Increase	2·643	·02
Criticism of others	Increase	2·095	·05

Self-criticism
Negative attitude to authority figures
Positive attitude to group members   Not significant
Negative attitude to non-specific authority

Test Results

Testing before and after treatment revealed few significant differences. In fact, the only positive test result showing any benefit of treatment was the significant increase in verbal I.Q. already referred to. This, however, in fact is an important finding showing, if confirmed, that low I.Q. is not necessarily a criterion of poor response to therapy.

Other tests which were included but gave no significant difference from test to test were the Matrices Test of Intelligence, HULL's Body-sway Test of primary suggestibility, an interests list, CROWN's Word Connection Test (1952) and the MAUDSLEY Medical Questionnaire. The significance of the results recorded in the previous paragraph can be assessed from the accompanying table, which gives a brief summary of the workshop control group during the year following the cessation of treatment. Figures for the third group, which was given a quite uncontrolled series of experiences

K

during treatment as mentioned above, are not comparable with the other two groups. If, however, we take the first two groups with their closely similar hospital routine during treatment and compare their subsequent record, the following facts emerge:

	Average number of days licensed to work away from hospital
Treatment Group	76·5
Workshop Control Group	44·0
Significance Level of Diff.	0·001

Conclusions

There are many shortcomings in such an investigation, but it appears to have established the fact that some certified defectives with subnormal I.Q.s and psychopathic tendencies can be much improved both in social attitudes and verbal facility by two sessions of weekly treatment. A more thorough-going attempt to improve their attitude, and one which offered a programme of training and rehabilitation as well as simply preparing them for emotional re-orientation, might have more far-reaching consequences. It is clear also that some scientific method offering at least the advantages of clear-cut definition and precise checking of results within circumscribed limits of interpretation, is necessary. An attempt has been made to use such a method in this investigation.

It may be said, as a consequence of the results described here, that the case of the defective delinquent is by no means hopeless. The appellation "incurable" can be applied to him in only a limited sense, and he is subject to improvement with treatment. In addition, he is disturbed by conditions which are disturbing to other patients, and may come within the range of treatment available for these others. He can be regarded as an acceptable patient for more elaborate and considered forms of treatment, instead of as the doubly hopeless case which he has been considered in the past, by reason, first, of his defect, and second, of his psychopathy.

The Unstable Feeble-Minded Defective

There is good reason to suppose that in whatever manner defectives who show behaviour problems are to be classified, whether as neurotics or psychopaths, constitutional inferiors or the socially deprived, the main problem is to estimate the degree to which they can be changed and assisted to readapt occupationally and socially. So far the limits within which progress can be reported are narrow. However, the very uncertainty of prediction, the undecided relationship between neurosis and performance, and above all the limited reliability of objective measures over long periods suggests that change, rather than permanence, may be the most characteristic feature of the mildly disturbed personality, no less among the defectives than among those of greater intelligence.

Too often a defective's current manner and behaviour is accepted as permanent. An assumption is made that he is constitutionally predisposed to neurosis or psychopathy. Sometimes this may be the case, but the assumption needs proof. In certain cases it will be found to be false. Investigations, planned on the basis of the constitutional assumption, seldom attempt to vary the conditions of life of the defective, and thus often give rise to the conclusion that change in behaviour is not to be expected. But if we plan experiments with an open mind, varying conditions, results similar to those reported here are sometimes forthcoming. It has been frequently noted that the level of social or scholastic competence of imbeciles is not necessarily consistent with the extent of cortical damage found in some patients. An imbecile with gross damage may show good adaptation and vice versa. In other words, there are at least two factors contributing to adjustment. Similarly, with the neurotic feeble-minded, it cannot be assumed that treatment will not be effective in assisting adjustment. Constitutional factors operate, but they will not necessarily be the sole determinants of behaviour.

Evidence from another study (O'CONNOR, 1951) not so far mentioned, gives support to the view that backwardness, far from being a handicap to therapy, may be in fact a symptom of the disorder which therapy is designed to alleviate. This study analysed the effect of asking a stable and unstable group of mental defectives of feeble-minded grade to repeat a test of manual dexterity for six trials. The findings showed certain statistically clear tendencies for the unstable to improve more than the stable. This finding was significant at the 5-per-cent level. This result is similar to that with the improvement in verbal I.Q. shown by patients after two hours of treatment per week for 32 sessions. Learning is often relatively great among those who start lowest on a scale.

Findings of this kind are held by the authors to argue a comparatively hopeful prognosis for the stabilization and ultimate employment of those who are emotionally disturbed in addition to being backward. Their problem, however, is a different one from that of the stable feeble-minded patient, and will not yield to simple occupational treatment. The possibility that it will yield at all is the chief claim which can be held to be established by the findings reported in this chapter.

CHAPTER TEN

ADMINISTRATIVE AND LEGAL IMPLICATIONS

THE EXISTING provision for mental defectives and the mentally subnormal has been described in Chapter 3. In summary the main facts as they affect England and Wales, with a population of 45 million people, are as follows:

In mental-deficiency hospitals at the end of 1954 there were 52,240 patients in residence, and a further 4,884 patients on licence. Hospitals were overcrowded, if patients on licence are excluded, by an average of 12 per cent, as judged by authorized standards of accommodation. There were 7,000 defectives awaiting hospital care. Since about 3,500 patients are admitted annually to mental deficiency hospitals the average waiting time at present would seem to be not less than two years. The average waiting time for imbeciles is probably longer than this, because both idiots and high-grade cases often receive priority. At the end of 1954, owing to the shortage of nurses, 1,336 hospital beds were out of use. A further 276 beds could not be used for other reasons.

There is a similar shortage of provision for imbeciles and idiots living at home. Of 21,537 imbeciles and idiots, both children and adults, regarded by local health authorities as being suitable for occupation centre or home training, only 12,658 were receiving training at the end of 1954. In December 1954 there were 29 local authorities with no occupation centres, and of these 15 authorities had no provision whatsoever for training defectives. There are great differences in the rates of ascertainment in different counties of England and Wales; these depend mainly upon the provision available for cases that have been ascertained. Where opportunities for training or admission to hospital scarcely exist, ascertainment rates tend to be low. The number who would benefit from training is certainly greater than the number of ascertained cases.

The figures given above relate to the mental-deficiency services. Mention should perhaps also be made of the shortage of provision for those educationally subnormal children who are deemed to need education in special schools. Because of the shortage of places, just over half of these children have been ascertained and places are available for less than one-third of the number presumed to require them. A distinction must however be made between the shortage of places in special schools, and the overall shortage of any form of training for imbeciles. Children who are ascertained as needing education in special schools remain in ordinary schools if there are no special schools for them to go to; imbeciles who are ascertained as needing occupation centre training remain at home, without any formal training, if there is no centre for them to attend. The figures for the educationally subnormal are given here only because educationally subnormal children are sometimes ascertained as feeble-minded when they leave school. Their education is, properly, a matter for the educational authorities, and they are not technically mentally defective.

In recent years the annual reports of the Ministry of Health have noted a steady expansion in the hospital and domiciliary services. The central authority is at present creating another 5,500 mental-deficiency beds, partly through the building of another 1,000-bed institution of the traditional sort, and partly by extensions to existing institutions. Waiting lists for institutional care are being cut; they now include "only those who genuinely need care at the reporting date", and not those who may require it in the future. The local health authorities are being encouraged by the Ministry to ascertain and make provision for more defectives living in the community. In the 1954 Report of the Ministry of Health, local health authorities are reported to be "beginning to make an impression on the problem" of providing occupation centre training.

Encouraging as these developments are, it must be added that with each extension of the mental-deficiency services has come an increase in manifest needs. Today, throughout the country as a whole, the gross overcrowding and barrack-like austerity of most mental-deficiency hospitals is still an effective means of keeping down the size of waiting lists. Parents hesitate to place their children except in cases of real necessity. Similarly, in many areas, the lack of occupation centres and sheltered workshops for imbeciles still discourages medical officers of health from ascertaining defectives who might benefit from training. At the present rate of expansion it would take many years before even occupation centre services were available in sufficient numbers to meet the needs of defectives living at home.

A more radical and more comprehensive attack on the problem is needed, one more in line with contemporary thinking on the social approach to mental health. In the following pages some of the general problems that arise in this field are discussed, in the light of our experience and research.

The Legal Concept of Mental Deficiency

In English law as it stands today mental deficiency is defined as "a condition of arrested or incomplete development of mind existing before the age of 18 years, whether arising from inherent causes or induced by disease or injury." Before a defective becomes "subject to be dealt with" (i.e. before legal procedures such as certification or placement under guardianship are undertaken), it has to be demonstrated that in addition to being mentally defective he satisfies certain social criteria, of which the following are the most important: he must be found ineducable or neglected, abandoned, or without visible means of support, or cruelly treated; or he must be in need of care or training which cannot be provided in his home. Alternatively, he must be found guilty of a criminal offence or ordered or found liable to be ordered to be sent to an approved school.

The present legal and administrative situation is complicated by the fact that the needs of the two great classes of persons cared for in mental-deficiency institutions—idiots and imbeciles on the one hand and those called feeble-minded on the other—differ greatly. While it may be administratively convenient to house them together, it is as misleading to call them by a common name as it would be classify the psychotic, the senile, the mentally defective, the epileptic and the neurotic under a common term such as "lunatic".

It is widely believed that special legislation in one form or another is needed to enable society to deal adequately with the problems posed by the mentally subnormal. The 1913 Mental Deficiency Act made possible the care of mental defectives at a time when there were few other social services to deal with the handicapped. Paradoxically, the Mental Deficiency Act, in the interests of the "liberty of the subject", made no real provision for care to be given on a voluntary basis, and no subsequent amending legislation has yet changed the semi-protective, semi-punitive character of our mental-deficiency laws. Much of the contemporary dissatisfaction with the mental-deficiency services arises from this fact, and a new Act is promised when the report of the present Royal Commission on the Law relating to Mental Illness and Mental Deficiency is published.

Many psychiatrists believe that the legal problems of mental deficiency could best be met by a comprehensive Mental Health Act which would include legislation affecting the mental defective as part of the general legislation covering all mental health problems. We, however, think that the scope both of the legislation and of the special services for the mentally defective could be drastically reduced, and that instead, other legislation and other services could, with some modification and extension, more adequately protect both the mentally defective and the community.

It can indeed be argued that there is no need at all for a special Mental Deficiency Act. Mentally defective children could come under the jurisdiction of the education, health and Home Office authorities, just as other handicapped or deprived children do, and the care of mentally defective adults could be arranged on a voluntary basis, as is the care given to old people, for example, and to others who need long-stay treatment in hospital. The few mental defectives who must be detained against their will, because of either criminal acts or anti-social, psycopathic conduct, or because they are a danger to themselves or others, could be held under appropriate sections of the law relating to criminals or the mentally ill.

Irrespective of how the legal issue is decided, services will still be needed to deal with the mentally handicapped, regardless of whether they continue to be called mentally defective or not. Some problems related to their care are discussed below.*

* A more general discussion of the administrative problem along lines similar to those proposed here is contained in the W.H.O. Report "The Mentally Subnormal Child" (1954).

Mentally Handicapped Children

The attitude of parents, and of the community, towards the handicapped is today very different from what it was at the time of the 1913 Mental Deficiency Act. Most families are now both willing and able to care for their mentally handicapped children if they are given some help in doing so. Today the basis of an adequate mental-deficiency service even for idiots and imbeciles must be laid in the community rather than the mental-deficiency hospital.

Because mental defectives living at home demand more attention from their families, and cause more work and expense than do normal children, special efforts are needed to lighten financial and domestic burdens. Such measures are expensive—but they are likely to be less expensive than institutional care.

Community services mean more than the provision of occupation centres and sheltered workshops for all who need them. Much needs to be done to help the families of defectives to understand their children, and to keep them at home where possible, without an abnormal disruption of family life. For infants and young children diagnostic clinics and observation units are needed. Mere diagnosis, or discovery, is, however, of little value if it is not supplemented by out-patient facilities and counselling services for parents and relatives. A few hospitals and local health authorities are today providing services of this sort. But the majority of hospitals, including psychiatric and children's hospitals, still do little to help parents either with their own psychological problems or with problems of management.*

Though there is a great shortage of occupation centres for mentally defective children, the value of occupation centre training is universally recognized. A strong case can be made for the proposal that the authorities should be obliged to provide occupation centre training for all mentally defective children; and attendance at such centres might well be made compulsory, unless the child is exempted on health grounds. Many authorities, including the National Union of Teachers (1955) and the British Medical Association (1955), believe that the education or training of all

---

* There are no beds in teaching hospitals set aside for mental defectives.

children, mentally defective as well as normal, should be the responsibility of the education, rather than the health authorities. Unified administration might enable children to be transferred more easily from school to occupation centre and back to school again when they show changes in mental growth.* A further advantage would be that the training and conditions of service of supervisors of occupation centres would become not inferior to those of teachers.

To enable mentally handicapped children to be properly educated, not only will a greater number of special school places need to be provided, but the range of special educational provision must be increased as well. No-one would maintain today that the blind, the deaf and the crippled, because they are all "physically defective" can be educated in a common school. Yet the needs of the "mentally defective", whether they be spastic or epileptic, psychotic or mongoloid, are presumed to be able to be met in a common occupation centre, too often staffed by inadequately trained supervisors, and housed in woefully unsatisfactory premises. There must be more specialization. To say this is not to say that children suffering from each of the many kinds of mental disability must be taught in a separate school. But at least the existence of different problems must be recognized, and the organization of school places and of the curriculum in a single school must be planned accordingly. Much more research is needed before this can be properly done; but a beginning could be made today.

Children who require residential care present further problems. It is likely that few idiot children would be kept at home if sufficient hospital care were available, and they should be able to be placed in children's hospitals without formality. Trainable imbecile children who need residential care should logically attend resi-

---

* Such transfers are still extraordinarily difficult in many parts of the country. Until the 1948 Education Act was passed no transfer of a child who had been declared ineducable back into the education system was possible. The certificate of ineducability was a permanent thing. How necessary it is that children can be transferred from one type of educational establishment to another can be illustrated from the experience of the Fountain Hospital, in which, during the last five years, 41 children from among the 200 who attend the occupation centre at one time have had their certificates of ineducability cancelled, and have been transferred from the care of mental-deficiency authorities to that of the education authorities in order to attend special schools.

dential schools if their education is to be under the jurisdiction of the education authorities. Such schools should be organized on lines similar to those of other hospital schools.

Educationally subnormal children should continue to be educated in special classes, or, where their disabilities or numbers warrant it, in special schools. Special provision should be made for the psychotic, and the emotionally maladjusted, and for all classes of physically handicapped children, irrespective of their mental grade. Under such a scheme as this both physically and mentally handicapped children would be dealt with under administrative arrangements designed primarily to cater for normal children, and the extension of the concept of normality which was begun by the Wood Committee in 1929 and given legal sanction in the 1944 Education Act would be completed.

Mental Deficiency in Adults

While the legal and administrative problems affecting mentally subnormal children appear to be relatively simple, the problem of mental deficiency in adulthood is more complex. In large part this is because of the extraordinary confusion that exists concerning the relationship between mental deficiency and delinquency, and the difficulties that arise in practice over the concept of moral deficiency. These difficulties were touched upon in Chapter 2, and again in later chapters in which the prevalence of mental disturbance in defectives was discussed, and an experimental study of the treatment of unstable mentally defective adolescents was described. A summary of literature on the relation between intellectual subnormality and crime and on the concept of psychopathy will be given now to relate the previous discussion to the legal and administrative problem of disposal and care.

Delinquency, Mental Deficiency and Psychopathy

Literature on the role of low intelligence in delinquency has recently been carefully reviewed by WOODWARD (1955). She points out that opinion on the relation of low intelligence to delinquency has changed considerably during the last 40 years. GORING's study of adult criminals led him to stress the causal importance of low intelligence; at the same time GODDARD in America concluded from his investigations that "low intelligence was the most important single factor in delinquency and crime". Instances of mental defect among delinquents ranged in studies collected by GODDARD from 25 to 90 per cent. In some small studies all delinquents were reported as being feeble-minded.

Since GODDARD'S time advances have been made both in sampling methods and in testing techniques. Recent American work, reviewed by WOODWARD, strongly suggests that when the distribution of I.Q.s of delinquents and non-delinquents living in comparable social conditions is compared, there is little or no difference between them, either in mean I.Q., or spread. It appears probable that where mean I.Q.s of delinquents are found to be below the average of the general population, the difference is accounted for by the association with delinquency of "that constellation of cultural factors which adversely affects the test scores". WOODWARD concludes her review by saying that low intelligence plays little or no part in delinquency in general. There is, however, some evidence that among those charged with sex offences, a higher proportion are mentally defective.*

Conclusions very similar to WOODWARD'S have been arrived at by LOWREY (1944) who has reviewed studies bearing on the relationship between mental deficiency and adult crime. Early work postulated that there was a close association between mental deficiency and crime; more recent work, using better tests, and taking cultural factors into account, shows this belief to be false. The most comprehensive study of the I.Q.s of criminals, according to LOWREY, is that by TULCHIN (1939).†

TULCHIN'S data included results of a 1920 survey of all inmates of Illinois penal and correctional institutions, and the routine psychometric testing of all who were admitted to these institutions from 1920 to the end of 1927. There were in all 10,413 prisoners tested. The standard procedure was to use the United States Army group intelligence tests, followed by individual testing of all those with low ratings and, in the latter part of the study, of all those who

---

* The sex offences committed by defectives are usually of a fairly harmless character, such as masturbation in public, or indecent exposure. Sexual assaults are fortunately rare.

† We have not been able to obtain TULCHIN'S book, and this summary follows LOWREY'S account of it.

could not read. With the exception of two groups, totalling 517, who made low scores and left the institution before individual examinations could be administered, all diagnoses of feeble-mindedness were based on scores obtained on individual tests. The data were subjected to detailed analysis and were compared with the test results reported for the Illinois Army draft. The major conclusions may be briefly summarized in LOWREY'S words:

"There are a number of important differences between the populations of the State Penitentiary and the State Reformatory, and some differences are shown between the 1920 survey results and the 1920–1927 study. But, so far as intelligence is concerned, the outstanding point is that *the percentages of inferior, average, and superior men in the prison population are extremely similar to those for the Illinois Army draft* (see TULCHIN, pp. 11–14). In point of fact, tests of nearly 5,000 men in the Reformatory showed a higher proportion of superior test results, and a smaller proportion of inferior, than did the Army draft. The entire institution population revealed 20·4 per cent inferior, 67·6 per cent average, and 11·9 per cent superior results, by comparison with 25·9 per cent inferior, 63·5 per cent average, and 10·6 per cent superior for the Army draft.

"With specific reference to the occurrence of inferior intelligence (mental ages below 10·9) the following percentages were found: Army draft, 25·9; 1920 survey of the penitentiaries, 24·4; seven-year admissions to the State Penitentiary, 23·4; similar study at the Reformatory, 15·0.

"The difference between the several groups is to be explained, according to the report, by differences in proportion of native-born whites, foreign-born, and Negroes in the Reformatory, the Penitentiary, and in the Army draft sample. The latter compares much more closely with the penitentiary population in average age and in distributions by nativity and race than it does with the reformatory group. Marked variations were found in intelligence distributions on comparing the several nativity and racial groups, and these must be taken into account when comparing intelligence distributions.

Cultural and educational factors were found to be definitely important in relation to test scores.

"It is of great significance, however, that for all nativity and racial groups, test results from the institution population approximate the distribution for the Army draft. In most instances where there is discrepancy, it is that the reformatory group shows a lower proportion of inferior test scores and a higher proportion of superior scores.

"The final conclusion, for our present purposes, is that a most adequate study has failed to produce evidence of any significant disproportion of test scores for male delinquents when compared with scores earned on the same tests by a draft group from the same areas. Some nativity and race groups in both series show quite high percentages of inferior ratings. As pointed out in the report (pp. 33-35), it would be absurd to label these large groups feeble-minded. The only direct comparison made for those of lowest rating (E, below MA 9-6, or I.Q. 60) is for the native-born whites, where the percentage for the Army and the penal group is approximately the same, 3·5 per cent to 4·0 per cent.

"Some relationship is found between the level of intelligence test scores and type of crime, in that the highest median scores were made by the men committed for fraud; the lowest by those committed for sex crimes. Individuals of all grades of intelligence were found in the six crime groups listed (fraud, robbery, larceny, burglary, murder, and sex crimes, in about that order for intelligence levels)."

As a result of the above, and similar studies, much less attention is today being paid to low intelligence as a determining factor in delinquency or crime. Interest has now shifted to emotional and conative aspects of the personality, and the term "moral imbecile" which found its way into the 1913 Mental Deficiency Act has been replaced by the term "psychopathic personality", or "aggressive psychopath", as a label to describe the anti-social delinquent of uncertain temper.

We doubt whether this change in name reflects any advance in knowledge of the supposed condition of psychopathy. Thus HENDERSON and GILLESPIE'S (1950) definition of psychopathy is as follows:

"We include under this title persons who have been from childhood or early youth habitually abnormal in their emotional reactions and conduct, but who do not reach, except episodically, a degree of abnormality amounting to certifiable insanity; they show no intellectual defect, as measured by the usual intelligence tests, and therefore cannot be classified in terms of the Mental Deficiency Act; and they do not benefit under prison treatment. They are not sufficiently well-balanced mentally to be at large, nor yet are they sufficiently involved as to be suitable for mental hospital care."

Although HENDERSON and GILLESPIE say that psychopaths show no intellectual defect, and therefore cannot be classified in terms of the Mental Deficiency Act, the definition given differs little from the definition of moral imbecile in the 1913 Act: "Persons who, from an early age, display some permanent mental defect, coupled with strong vicious or criminal propensities, on which punishment has had little or no deterrent effect." It is, moreover, the opinion both of TREDGOLD (1949) and of the Board of Control (1954) that low intelligence is not a necessary concomitant of mental deficiency, and that therefore those whom HENDERSON and GILLESPIE refer to as psychopaths may, in certain cases, fall within the province of the Mental Deficiency Act.

That there is no agreement among psychiatrists as to the definition of psychopathy or its cause can be seen by consulting a book such as WALLIN'S (1949) which reviews the literature on the subject. The practical implications of the confusion become clear when one attempts to ascertain what proportion of criminals are psychopathic as judged by psychiatrists. WALLIN presents the following table (Table 34).

To these figures may be added MINSKI'S (1955) opinion that "90 per cent or more of children who commit a serious offence and go through approved schools and Borstal are potential if not actual psychopaths at that age," and that of KARPMAN (1948) who speaks of "the myth of the psychopathic personality", and who would place all or nearly all persons diagnosed by some other psychiatrists as psychopathic in quite different categories, with supposedly different aetiology and prognosis, and for whom different forms of treatment would be proposed.

Table 34

Type of Case	Year	Authority	Per cent Psychopathic
350 adult criminals (Boston Municipal Courts)	1915	ANDERSON	24·3
400 women criminals (Mass. Reformatory)	1915	SPAULDING	7·7*
608 men prisoners (Sing Sing)	1918	GLUECK	18·9
Women criminals (Ill. Reformatory)	1919–29	SUTHERLAND	88·3
Offenders in Detroit (Recorders Court)	1924	RAPHAEL	36·0
2,000 juvenile delinquents (Boston, Judge Baker Foundation)	1927	HEALY and BRONNER	2·8
1,000 juvenile delinquents (follow-up of Judge Baker Foundation cases)	1934	SHELDON and ELEANOR GLUECK	1·9†
Federal penitentiary criminals (Lewisburg, Penna.)	1937	WHOLEY	14·0
9,958 prisoners convicted in the Court of General Sessions, New York City		BROMBERG and THOMPSON	6·9

* Marked neuropathic or psychopathic cases.
† Exclusive of "constitutional inferiors".

Among those psychiatrists who recognize the concept of psychopathic personality, there are in addition wide divergences of opinion as to the curability of the condition. Some psychiatrists, such as MAXWELL JONES (1955), take an optimistic view of prognosis, whereas others, such as MINSKI—working in the same hospital—take an exceedingly pessimistic one.

We are not concerned with the correctness of these different conceptions—clearly the problem is not solved, and possibly it has not even been formulated in a manner which would make it possible to be solved. What is important from a medico-legal viewpoint is the fact of complete disagreement among the experts as to what constitutes psychopathy, what is the prevalence of the condition, and on what grounds psychopaths should be detained against their will. In these circumstances we can see no good grounds for advocating special legislation for psychopaths, who might best be dealt with under the existing penal code, when they break the law.* There appears even less justification for including psychopathy, or moral delinquency, as one of the categories of mental deficiency, though some mentally subnormal delinquents might benefit from the kind of treatment now available to other unstable criminals in the provisions of the Criminal Justice Act.

Once the treatment of mental deficiency can be rid of its association with moral deficiency, it should be possible to devise a reasonable and humane approach to the problems of the mentally subnormal, without resort to compulsion or detention.

Idiot and Imbecile Adults

The number of idiots who survive to adolescence is extremely small, and it is only rarely that they continue to be kept at home in adult life. Where parents do look after idiot children they should be given every assistance; little can be done for the defectives themselves.

With imbeciles the situation is rather different. The studies described in Chapter 7 indicate that promising results can be obtained, even with severely handicapped imbecile adults who have had few opportunities and little training from their earliest years. More research is needed on how *work*—which is not the same thing as occupational therapy—can be organized so as to enable as many imbeciles as possible to become employed. A few workshops in Holland (CARSTAIRS, CLARK and O'CONNOR, 1955) show something of the possibilities of this kind of employment. Vocational guidance and training and sheltered workshops could, we believe, ensure that effective use was made of the potentialities of large numbers of adult imbeciles.

Substantial numbers of adolescent and adult imbeciles need residential care, either in hospital with adequate provision for

---

* If one studies the case histories of the more notorious "aggressive psychopaths" of recent years—Heath, Haigh, Straffen and the like—what emerges most clearly is that their psychopathy became obvious only in retrospect. Even if there had been special legislation making possible the detention of "aggressive psychopaths" men such as these would not have been prevented by it from committing the crimes they did.

employment, or in hostels with sheltered workshops nearby. At present no hostels associated with sheltered workshops exist for imbeciles. Experimental units would provide information as to their usefulness and desirability. For imbeciles who had lived a substantial part of their lives in the community and were used to working in sheltered employment, hostels might offer a more kindly environment, less cut off from society than the large mental-deficiency hospital, when their parents died or were unable to continue to look after them.

Feeble-minded Adults Living in the Community

The literature already reviewed in Chapter 8 shows that the great majority of educationally subnormal school-leavers can take their place along with other adolescents at the work bench or counter. Those who find difficulty in keeping a job need help, and this should be given through the Youth Employment Bureaux by officers and social workers with special knowledge of the problems of the mentally subnormal. Many studies have shown that a some-what higher proportion of mentally subnormal adolescents than of more gifted young people find it difficult to obtain suitable work. Sometimes their difficulties are caused by their being placed in jobs which they find too complex; sometimes the supervision is inadequate, and sometimes the young people themselves need further training before they can work in the open market. A small proportion of feeble-minded adolescents is too unstable to work in other than sheltered workshops. Much research still needs to be done to find answers to the many detailed questions regarding their training and employment. What can be said today is that where good vocational guidance services exist, supplemented by adequate social work, finding suitable employment for educationally subnormal school-leavers gives rise to few problems. The present tendency to deal with the needs of the educationally subnormal through general youth employment and social services is a healthy one, but the services need more trained staff to cope with their problems.

Hostel and Institutional Care

The special and complex problems of hostel and institutional care, and the problem of compulsion will only be touched upon here. A discussion of some of the legal aspects of mental deficiency has been given elsewhere. (TIZARD, 1955.)

Some authorities believe that the comprehensive colony which houses defectives of all ages and grades cannot provide satisfactory care for defectives. MACMAHON (1955), has expressed this point of view very forcibly:

"Low-grade defect appears to be almost invariably deter-mined by pathological abnormalities, related, in various ways, to such low mental (and often other) potentials, that the most humane and devoted care, supplemented by all available scientific resources, cannot bring the social prognosis of idiots and most imbeciles within the socially tolerable range. The vast majority of the feeble-minded, however, are merely low-grade normals, and as a rule they function within the normal range in the community. Those unfortunate enough in their nurture to need mental-deficiency hospital care are a minority: but most of them possess the same potentials as the uncertified and have therefore fair prospects of successful social habilita-tion and return to the community capable, in many instances, of fending for themselves.

"It is important to note, however, that when either of these two regimens is applied independently of the other, a fair degree of success may be achieved; but, in large institutions with mixed populations, the adequate segregation of grades, classes and types is usually quite impracticable—for this, and other reasons, modifications and compromises become neces-sary, and these in turn have such prejudicial effects that they militate against the best interests of high and low-grade cases alike."

MACMAHON'S viewpoint is supported by some other witnesses who have appeared before the Royal Commission on the Law Relating to Mental Illness and Mental Deficiency. The memor-andum of the British Psychological Society (1955) contains the following graphic description of the consequences of that mixture of grade which it is difficult to avoid at present in a large compre-hensive institution: "The effects of mixing grades can be seen at their worst in children's wards where, owing to lack of numbers, segregation by grade is virtually impossible. Here the idiot, the

imbecile and the feeble-minded child (sometimes of potential
normality) may play together; the epileptic, the deaf and dumb,
the spastic and the near-psychotic are cared for by a changing staff
inadequate in number and often in quality.* Inevitably, under
such conditions, individual progress may be very adversely
affected. With older patients an attempt at segregation by grade is
made, but not unnaturally the feeble-minded resent being classed
with idiots and imbeciles. Moreover, the pay or conditions of
service often fail to attract adequate numbers of nursing staff, and
many 'part-timers' are employed, or, worse still, the care of the
lower-grade and more helpless patients is relegated *faute de mieux*
to patients of higher grade.''

Writing from a different standpoint, CROSS (1954) in his survey
of mental-deficiency hospitals in the Birmingham region, makes the
criticism that the comprehensive colony is wasteful of medical
staff.

These criticisms of our present administrative policy based on
the comprehensive colony have been given in some detail because
they suggest the need for a more critical review of these strengths
and weaknesses than has been undertaken in recent years. There is,
it is true, no lack of authoritative support for the comprehensive
colony, but the only evaluation of its functioning which has appeared
since the Wood Report of 1929 was contained in a Departmental
Report published in 1931 (Board of Control, 1931).

We ourselves have one criticism to make of existing institutions
for mental defectives considered as training colonies—licence and
discharge seem unnecessarily restricted. It is not possible to prove
this point, since whether any patient is able to be sent on licence
must, in part, be a matter of opinion. What can, however, be said,
is that institutional policy regarding the sending of patients on
licence seems to be affected by the proportion of high-grade

* CROSS (1954) gives the following averages for the Birmingham region of the
numbers of patients in children's wards in mental-deficiency hospitals who are
looked after by one nurse during the day and night:

Time	Grade of Ward			
	High	Medium	Low	All
Day	16	14	10	11
Night	31	55	41	43

patients on the books of a particular colony. If a high proportion of the patients is of low grade, few of the *high-grade* patients are sent on licence, either because they are needed to help run the institution, or because the authorities fail to appreciate the opportunities available today for placing defectives at work in the community, or because institutions are not staffed in such a way as to enable them to spend time on this activity.

This point can be illustrated by data obtained from our survey of patients in hospitals in the London area. The proportion of male and female patients in each of seven institutions who were of high grade (i.e. classified as feeble-minded according to hospital records) was calculated for each hospital, as was the proportion of feeble-minded patients who were on daily or resident licence. Thus, in one hospital 58 per cent of the total population was classified as feeble-minded, and 32 per cent of these patients were on licence when the survey was undertaken. In a second hospital 37 per cent of male patients were high-grade, and fewer than 10 per cent of these patients were on licence. The hospitals were ranked according to the percentage of patients who were of high grade, and again according to the percentage of high-grade patients who were on licence. Had there been no relationship between these data there would have been no correlation between the two rankings. In fact there was a correlation of 0·82 between the proportions of high-grade male patients on the books of the different hospitals and the porportion of these patients on licence. For female patients the correlation between the rankings was 0·78. These correlations are unlikely to be spurious, and they support the hypothesis proposed. While it is possible that other explanations could account for these results, the explanation given here seems a plausible one. One might perhaps go further and suggest that if the high-grade patients had been treated as adults who needed care, rather than as defectives under detention, the proportion thought fit to work in the community might have been higher still.

It may be for this reason that patients who are discharged from the provisions of the Mental Deficiency Acts spend so long in hospital beforehand. Table 35 gives the figures for length of stay of patients discharged from hospitals in 1951.

Of 572 males discharged, 85 per cent were feeble-minded and

*Table 35. Discharges from Mental-Deficiency Hospitals in 1951 by
Length of Stay in Hospital before Discharge**

	0	1 –	2 –	3 –	5 –	10 –	15 –	20	25 –	30 +	Total
Males	27	38	50	78	169	115	61	18	12	4	572
Females	30	34	38	76	152	123	96	48	30	6	633

8 per cent imbeciles; the proportions of females were 84 and 8
respectively. 94 per cent of the males and 96 per cent of the
females discharged were aged 16 and over. The median period of
stay was about 7 years 9 months for men and 9 years 7 months for
women. Economies of scale obtained by using large units are likely
to be offset if the turnover of patients is slower than it would be
under a different system.

Two alternatives to the large comprehensive colony have been
proposed. They are large hospitals with a more homogenous population of either the feeble-minded or of idiots and imbeciles, and
smaller hostels for selected groups of defectives. Both proposals
merit consideration. The large "classified" institution was favoured
by the London County Council before the war, some institutions
being used primarily for high-grade patients, while others housed
mainly low-grade defectives. The chief objections to existing large-
scale classified institutions are perhaps that the size of the units is
so large, and that the remoteness of such places from the towns and
cities from which the patients come makes rehabilitation and the
finding of suitable work more difficult than they would otherwise
be.

An objection which is sometimes raised is that an institution
which cared only for imbeciles and idiots would be such a depress-
ing place to work in that it would be impossible to staff. (While this
is not a positive argument in favour of the comprehensive institution it would, if valid, rule out institutions containing only low-
grade patients.) This is fortunately not true. Most medical witnesses who have appeared before the Royal Commission have
expressed the view that the presence of high-grade patients in
their institutions does not make their problem of finding staff any

* From the Registrar General's *Statistical Review of England and Wales for
the Two Years* 1950–1951.

easier, though it may assist them in the running of their hospitals. Moreover, those hospitals which take mainly low-grade patients are not inevitably worse off for staff than are other hospitals. The comprehensive colony is not the answer to the problem of nurse recruitment.

While reconsideration of the policy of the classified as against the comprehensive colony may be desirable, it is usually agreed that hostel care, if it were practicable, would be more satisfactory than care in a large institution.

There would probably be more hostels, were local authorities not deterred from establishing them by fears as to their running costs. We, however, are not certain that the economic costs of hostel care, at least of the feeble-minded, would differ greatly from institution costs. For example, the Rowntree survey of homes for old people, whose problems are in many ways comparable with those posed by high-grade institutional defectives, maintained that "overheads cease to have an undue influence on the cost per resident when the numbers reach 30 to 35." They advocated highly classified institutions of medium size as an interim measure until small houses can be built, rather than large comprehensive institutions for old people with widely differing needs. Other data support the belief that the running costs of small institutions need not be greater than those of large ones. In a small enquiry which we carried out some years ago, information was obtained from a number of voluntary societies who run homes or hostels for young people. One of these societies, The Fellowship of St. Christopher, an Anglican Foundation, provided at that time homes for about 130 boys between the ages of 15 and 18, who for one reason or another were not being looked after by their parents. The Fellowship had four hostels, each containing about 30 boys. Large houses with large gardens had been converted for the purpose. Each hostel had a dining room and sitting rooms, a quiet room and a gymnasium (made out of an old conservatory). The boys slept in bedrooms with from three to six beds in each. The treasurer of the Fellowship reported in the Annual Report that for the year ending 31st January 1951, "the cost of maintaining a boy in one of the Fellowship's houses after making provision for all expenses, including the ordinary running repairs to the houses, and office and administration expenses (15 per cent of the total), and excluding amounts recovered from the boy or his sponsor, is approximately £137 per annum." This is £2 12s. 8d. per week. The local authorities made up the contribution for each boy after the boy had paid a proportion of his wages, to £3 a week, which during 1951 was regarded as a satisfactory figure for maintenance.

Comparable data about costs were obtained from the Salvation Army Welfare Department. Costs for old people in Salvation Army Homes, holding between 25 and 35 residents during 1951, varied from £2 2s. to £3. The average cost was about £2 10s. One Salvation Army Home for old people which was visited contained 26 senile men. The problems of managing them and attending to their needs cannot have been less easy than those involved in looking after defectives, and the residents themselves did little to help by way of housework or chores. Nonetheless the house was run at an average cost per head of £2 10s. a week.

These figures suggest that from an economic point of view it should be possible to run small hostels for mental defectives without undue cost. Daily costs per head need be no higher than those incurred in keeping these patients in colonies, and might even be cheaper. If the average period of residence was less in a hostel than in a colony, as is anticipated, total costs might be considerably less than those of institutions.

We think that if society, instead of retaining under certificate feeble-minded persons who cannot live at home, provided care on a voluntary basis, the need for compulsion would largely disappear. The work of HILLIARD (1954) of the Fountain Hospital, indicates that even those who are generally thought to be the most difficult patients at present certified as mentally defective, namely, high-grade feeble-minded women with I.Q.s ranging from 55 to 110, can be successfully rehabilitated with a minimum of compulsion if they are wisely treated. A voluntary system of care, supplemented only by sanctions applied to those who are found guilty of offences against the law, might be most suited to the needs of the mentally subnormal.

For these reasons we think that a reablement programme for the feeble-minded who cannot live at home can best be carried out using a hostel system. If several hostels were in the same neighbourhood, a sheltered workshop could be set up in the grounds of one of them at which patients who needed occupational training could be trained on work subcontracted from firms in the locality. Following training, they might be sent to those same firms if they so desired it. Being with older persons who were themselves working would serve as an example to adolescents, and to the unstable and immature. Such hostels could be run either by nurses, or by lay staff. A consultant psychiatrist, possibly from a neighbouring hospital, might give advice and therapy, and additional medical treatment could be obtained from general practitioners through the National Health Service.

CHAPTER ELEVEN
CONCLUSIONS

THE OBSERVATIONS made in the first three chapters on the care of mental defectives suggest that since the passing of the 1913 Mental Deficiency Act there has been an increasing emphasis on community provision. Among the factors responsible for this are full employment and practical difficulties associated with hospital staffing. In recent years there has been a reconsideration of the supposed social danger of allowing defectives to mix freely in the community. This danger is less acutely felt today than it was in the first decade of the century.

The many studies referred to in Chapter 4 show that the majority of feeble-minded persons can make a tolerably good social adjustment in the community. That these studies show many inconsistencies is due partly to differences in the samples studied and partly to the fact that investigators have followed up defectives during different economic periods. In times of heavy unemployment there is no doubt that many defectives have great occupational difficulties. In BALLER'S 1936 investigation 42 per cent of a mentally subnormal group had some dependence on relief during the depression, as compared with 16 per cent of a control group of people of average intelligence. In periods of full employment, however, it is relatively easy to place defectives in jobs. The economic contribution which they can make is considerable as well as being of great therapeutic value.

It is argued that the kind of work offered in hospitals at present may not be the best form of treatment, and is probably not economical. At the same time, to house mental defectives in comprehensive colonies has a number of disadvantages. Some of these were further emphasized in Chapter 10. On the whole, the feeble-minded patient has few opportunities of being sent on licence if he is in a mixed colony under present circumstances. The information given in Chapter 10 suggests that his presence in a comprehensive colony may militate against his rehabilitation, however good may be the intentions of the hospital.

162

The question of deciding which defectives should be given opportunities for working out from such a hospital has been discussed in Chapters 4 and 5. The results indicate that selection by psychometric tests is not practicable. The reasons for this fact are twofold. Firstly, social circumstances which change continuously account for a great deal of the uncertainty of prediction. A prediction based on psychological traits may, because of changes in employment possibilities, have little practical value. A success versus failure level on a criterion of work success may fluctuate a great deal with economic change. However good a battery of tests may be, under these circumstances it is likely to be ineffective as a predicting instrument. Secondly, the validity of predictions based on the assessment of psychological qualities depends upon the assumption that individuals do not change in certain cognitive, conative or affective aspects of their measurable constitution. Our studies, however, suggest that such changes do take place in qualities of personality. They would seem to be more variable than general cognitive or specific cognitive and motor abilities.

Another question discussed in Chapters 4 and 5 arises from such considerations. If the possibility of successfully using tests or other measures for individual guidance is small at present, we must conclude that the only proper course is to make every opportunity for employment available to all the feeble-minded in hospitals. To confine a neurotic defective to hospital may be to deny him an opportunity which, if granted, would act as a treatment. Mild emotional instability seems to clear up in many feeble-minded defectives sent on licence from hospital. There are, however, a few feeble-minded patients who are so severely neurotic that they need special treatment before being fit for outside employment. An approach to the problem of their treatment is described in Chapter 9.

Leaving aside the care of such special cases, Chapters 6 and 7 discuss the success of investigations into the training and employment of defectives, both feeble-minded and imbecile. The chief conclusion from these studies is that mental deficiency, whilst disabling in part, is not so disabling that training and correct guidance cannot enable the feeble-minded to work in the community, and large numbers of imbeciles in sheltered workshops.

In a hospital workshop defectives can be trained to do mechanical repetitive tasks to a speed between 50 per cent and 70 per cent of normal. The problems of setting up such a workshop and obtaining sub-contracts from firms have been discussed fully in Chapter 6. The main problem is to win confidence of both the patients and the works managers of firms. At a later stage in our investigations this proved easier than it did at the beginning, when we ourselves were not entirely convinced that the projects could succeed.

The effect of regular paid work on both the output and behaviour of feeble-minded patients is very great in many cases. Their tolerance of frustration improves, self-confidence is increased, and the widening of their life interests by contact with the outside world is notable for its extent and vigour. Among other hospitals, Darenth Park and the Manor have created a body of practical experience in the work training of the feeble-minded and imbeciles. Systems of payment and supervision vary somewhat at present. The view supported by our experiments is that standard rates should be paid for work done and that much attention should be paid to the problems of supervision and the training of supervisors.

The learning capacity of the feeble-minded and imbecile is discussed in Chapter 7. Though little is known about the limits of capacity of the mentally subnormal, the study of learning and of training must be regarded as basic to our understanding of their psychology. The immense amount of work done on intelligence testing has, to some extent, led to neglect of the more fundamental problems of cognition.

Although imbeciles and the feeble-minded do not achieve normal levels of work in all cases, great improvement does take place. Relative improvement may be greater among imbeciles than among the feeble-minded, even though their final level of performance may remain lower. It was noted that some patients who had apparently reached a plateau of performance in hospital immediately improved to a still higher level when placed among normal workers in a factory.

The success of training conducted in the workshops is matched by the success achieved by patients sent out to work on a building site. Figures are quoted in Chapter 8. It must be added that the policy of placing patients on licence has had a striking success in those hospitals in which an active policy has been followed.

The investigations reported in previous chapters and the literature reviewed have led us to conclude that some of the difficulties inherent in the hospital care of the feeble-minded and imbeciles might be overcome if more provision were made for extra-mural care. The outline of proposals of this kind are given in Chapter 10, where the legal and administrative problems of such a plan are examined.

In essence, these amount to suggesting the need for a system of voluntary care, with more hostels and training centres for the feeble-minded, and the provision of more supervisory staff to offer guidance to those educationally subnormal school-leavers who might otherwise be certified as feeble-minded under the present Acts. For the imbecile the trend towards an increase in occupation centres is regarded as a healthy one and, in addition, we would consider it desirable to provide hostels and sheltered workshops on a larger scale for adult imbeciles. Many idiots and some imbeciles need hospital care, but, as they constitute a very small proportion of the mentally subnormal, existing hospital accommodation should be adequate for their needs.

The proposals outlined in Chapter 10 would entail a fundamental revision of our mental-deficiency services. These proposals will undoubtedly be regarded by some as too radical. In the text an attempt has been made to justify them with experimental results. In some respects, this has been successful, and in others the results are less complete. Most of the investigations are consistent in their findings, although some inconsistencies point to need for further research. For example, the problem of motivation needs further investigation. It is apparent, too, that much has yet to be done to examine the mechanics of performance improvement among the mentally subnormal. Likewise, many more studies are needed on the treatment of neurotic defectives. Our research has been fuller on the side of occupational than of social adaptation. More basic prophylactic work is needed so that training and preparation for adult life can be undertaken at earlier ages. The problem is an urgent one and the official and popular interest which it now arouses would appear to justify further research, in addition to a revision of the law and an extension of the community services.

APPENDIX

QUANTIFIED UNSTABLE HISTORY MEASURE

AN UNSTABLE history score or what was regarded as a score of deviant behaviour was taken as a criterion of instability on the assumption that the kind of instability which leads to social maladjustment was important to the investigation. Possible objections to a behaviour score of this kind were recognized in constructing the scale, but it was thought that the advantages of an objective criterion outweighed most of these disadvantages. Use was necessarily made of the records in the hospital record books kept in the central office. The only contributory scores were therefore those to be found in these books. Included in these records were:

Escapes
Sickness
Presence of enuresis
Presence in special supervision ward
Granting of parole

When a boy had been ill or had been punished by being confined to a detention ward, or when enuresis was recorded, this was noted for the year ending November 1950. Such occurrences were given a positive score of 10. When parole was granted, this fact was noted and a negative score of 10 allotted. As records for escapes were readily available over longer periods in some cases than others, they were standardized for a hypothetical 10-year period. All scores were thus based on a 10-year period. In some cases boys were neither enuretic, had had no recent sickness, had never escaped, nor been placed in a punishment ward, but had been granted parole. In this case they would be scored minus 10. In all cases therefore, a constant of 10 was added to scores to avoid the minus measures.

On this system all high scores represent lack of conformity to 'good' social behaviour, and low scores represent adjustment to hospital life. Whether or not conformity to hospital routine is a

166

sign of social adjustment is arguable, but in general it is felt that most of the measures show the presence or absence of an ability to find the correct solution to the problem of social adjustment. This was shown to some extent in the correlation between this measure and the subsequent work success of each patient.

The reason for the inclusion of each item is obvious in most cases. In two, enuresis and sickness, measures were included despite the fact that other reasons than social maladjustment may have been the cause. In the case of enuresis the psychiatrist was of the opinion that the symptom was caused in the few cases where it was found, by instability. In the case of sickness, observation showed that most of the complaints recorded were trivial, and seemed to represent an attempt on the part of the boy who reported ill, to escape from duties or workshop training. It was felt that sickness might therefore be included as a measure of minor maladjustment. In some cases no doubt boys' scores would be increased because of genuine complaints and no attempt was made to compensate for such a possibility because records were inadequate to ensure the accuracy of such allowances.

The contribution of each part score to the predictive value of the total has yet to be determined.

REFERENCES

ABEL, T. M. (1925) "Tested mentality as related to success in skilled trade training." Thesis submitted for Ph.D. Degree, Columbia University.

ATTENBOROUGH, H. J., and FARBER, M. (1934) "The relationship between intelligence mechanical ability and manual dexterity in special school children." *Brit. J. educ. Psychol.* **4**, 140–61.

BALLER, W. R. (1936) "A study of the present social status of a group of adults who, when they were in elementary schools, were classified as mentally deficient." *Genet. Psychol. Monogr.* **18**, 165–244.

BICE, H. V. (1948) "A decade in psychology." *Amer. J. ment. Def.* **53**, 57–60.

BICKMORE, A. (1913) *Industries for the Feeble-Minded and Imbecile.* London.

BIJOU, I. W., AINSWORTH, H. H., and STOCKEY, M. R. (1943) "The social adjustment of mentally retarded girls paroled from Wayne County Training School." *Amer. J. ment. Def.* **47**, 422–8.

BINET, A., and SIMON, Th. (1907) *Les Enfants Anormaux.* Libraire Armand Colin, Paris.

BINET, A., and SIMON, Th. (1914) *Mentally Defective Children* (trans. MARGARET DRUMMOND). Edward Arnold, London.

BRADY, M. (1948) "Suggestibility and persistence in epileptics and mental defectives." *J. ment. Sci.* **94**, 444–51.

BRITISH MEDICAL ASSOCIATION (1955) *Minutes of Evidence of the Royal Commission on the Law Relating to Mental Illness and Mental Deficiency,* 26th day. Her Majesty's Stationery Office, London.

BROMBERG, W. (1948) *Crime and the Mind.* Lippincott, Philadelphia.

BURT, C. (1922) *Mental and Scholastic Tests.* P. S. King, London.

BURT, C. (1937) *The Subnormal Mind* (2nd ed.). Oxford Univ. Press.

BURT, C. (1940) *Factors of the Mind.* University of London Press.

BURT, C. (1944) "The factorial study of physical types." *Man.* **72**, 82–6

BURT, C. (1946) *The Backward Child* (2nd ed.). University of London Press.

CARSTAIRS, G. M., CLARK, D. H., and O'CONNOR, N. (1955) "Occupational Treatment of Chronic Psychotics." *Lancet.* **2**, 1025–30.

CHARLES, D. C. (1953) "Abilities and accomplishments of persons earlier judged to be mentally defective." *Genet. Psych. Monog.* **47**, 3–71.

CLARKE, A. D. B., and CLARKE, A. M. (1953) "How constant is the I.Q.?" *Lancet.* **2**, 877.

CLARKE, A. D. B., HERMELIN, and FLIESS (1955) "Adult Imbeciles: Their Abilities and Trainability." *Lancet.* **2**, 337–9.

COAKLEY, F. A. (1945) "A Study of feebleminded wards employed in war industries." *Amer. J. ment. Def.* **50**, 301–6.

COTZIN, M. (1948) "Group psychotherapy with mentally defective problem boys." *Amer. J. ment. Def.* **53**, 268–83.

Cox, J. W. (1934) *Manual Skill*. Cambridge Univ. Press.

Cross, K. W. (1954) "A survey of mental hospitals and mental deficiency institutions in the Birmingham Region (ii. Mental deficiency institutions)." *Brit. J. prev. Soc. Med.* 8, 162–71.

Crown, S. (1952) "The word connexion list as a diagnostic test: norms and validation." *Brit. J. Psychol.* 43, 103–12.

Culpin, M., and Smith, May (1930) The nervous temperament. *Rep. industr. Hlth. Res. Board (Pink Reports)*. No. 61. Her Majesty's Stationery Office, London.

Cureton, T. K. (1935) "*Endurance of Young Men*." Monograph of the Society for Research in Child Development, Vol. X, 1.

Curran, D., and Guttmann, E. (1946) *Psychological Medicine*. Livingstone, Edinburgh.

Dahlberg, G. (1937) "On the frequency of mental deficiency." *Upsala Läkareforenings Fördhandlingar*. 5, 439.

Darrow, G. W., and Heath, L. L. (1932) Reaction tendencies relating to personality, in *Studies in the Dynamics of Behaviour* (K. S. Lashley, ed.). University of Chicago Press.

Davis, D. R. (1948) *Pilot Error: Some Laboratory Experiments*. Her Majesty's Stationery Office, London.

Davis, D. R. (1949) "The disorder of skill responsible for accidents." *Quarterly J. exp. Psychol.* 1, 136–42.

Dayton, N. (1931) "Mortality in mental deficiency over a 14 year period." *Proc. & Addr. Amer. Ass. for the study of the Feebleminded*, Philadelphia. 36, 127–205. (*Psychol. Abstr.* 1932. 6, No. 385.)

Dayton, N. A. (1939) *Report of the Mental Deficiency Committee*. Public Document 117. Commonwealth of Massachusetts.

Dearborn, W. F., and Rothney, J. W. H. (1941) *Predicting the Child's Development*. Sci. Art. Publishers, Cambridge, Mass.

Dewan, J. G. (1948) "Intelligence and emotional stability." *Amer. J. Psychiat.* 104, 548–54.

Doll, E. J. (1932) *Research opportunities at Vineland training school*. *Vineland Publications No.* 2. Vineland N.J.

Duncan, A. G. (1936) "Mental deficiency and manic depressive insanity." *J. ment. Sci.* 82, 635.

Enke, W. (1930) *Die psychometrik der konstitutionstypen*. Borth, Liepzig. (Quoted by Eysenck, H. J., in *The Scientific Study of Personality*.)

Esher, F. J. S. (1941) "The mental defective in the army." *Brit. Med. J.* 2, 187–90.

Eysenck, H. J. (1943) "Suggestibility and hypnosis." *Proc. Roy. Soc. Med.* 36, 349–54.

Eysenck, H. J. (1947) *The Dimensions of Personality*. Kegan Paul, London.

Eysenck, H. J. (1950) "Personality tests: 1944–1949," in *Recent Progress in Psychiatry* (G. W. T. H. Fleming, ed.). Churchill, London.

M

EYSENCK, H. J. (1952) *The Scientific Study of Personality*. Routledge & Kegan Paul, London.

EYSENCK, H. J. (1953) "The logical basis of factor analysis." *Amer. Psychologist.* **8**, 105–14.

EYSENCK, H. J., and FURNEAUX, W. D. (1945) "Primary and secondary suggestibility." *J. Exp. Psychol.* **35**, 485–503.

EYSENCK, H. J., and REES, W. L. L. (1945) "States of heightened suggestibility; narcosis." *J. ment. Sci.* **91**, 301–10.

FALLS, R. P., and BLAKE, R. R. (1948) "A quantitative analysis of the picture frustration study." *J. Pers.* **16**, 320–5.

FESSARD, A., LANGIER, H., and NOEL, S. (1933) "Sur un indice de tenacité au cours de travail statique." *Trav. Hum.* **1**, 32–48.

FITZPATRICK, F. K. (1955) An investigation bearing on the laws relating to feeblemindedness, and their application. *Brit. J. educ. Psychol.* **25**, 117–22.

FOULDS, G. A. (1944) The mental defective and agriculture. *Occup. Psychol.* **18**, 142–7.

FOULDS, G. A. (1945) The child-family relationship and the frustration types among mental defectives and juvenile delinquents. *Brit. J. Med. Psychol.* **20**, 255–60.

FOULKES, S. H. (1948) *Introduction to Group Analytic Psychotherapy*. Heinemann, London.

FRASER, RUSSELL (1947) *The Incidence of Neurosis Among Factory Workers*. Rep. Indr. Hlth. Res. Board (Pink Reports). No. 90. Her Majesty's Stationery Office, London.

FREEMAN, G. L., and KATZOFF, E. T. (1942) "Individual differences in physiological reactions to stimulation and their relation to other measures of emotionality." *J. Exp. Psychol.* **31**, 527–37.

FREMMING, K. H. (1951) *The expectation of mental infirmity in a sample of the Danish population*. Eugenics Soc.: Cassell, London.

FRIEDLANDER, K. (1947) *The Psychoanalytic Approach to Juvenile Delinquency*. Kegan Paul, London.

GHISELLI, E. E., and BROWN, C. W. (1948) *Personnel and Industrial Psychology*. McGraw-Hill, New York.

GLASSMAN, L. A. (1942–43) *Smith. Coll. Studies in Social Work*, Vol. 13.

GLOVER, E. (1944) *The Diagnosis and Treatment of Delinquency*. Institute for the Study and Treatment of Delinquency, London.

GORDON, S., O'CONNOR, N., and TIZARD, J. (1954) "Some effects of incentives on the performance of imbeciles." *Brit. J. Psychol.* **45**, 277–87.

GOULD, R. (1939) "An experimental analysis of level of aspiration." *Genet. Psychol. Monog.* **21**, 1–116.

GOULD, R. (1941) "Some sociological determinants of goal strivings." *J. Soc. Psychol.* **13**, 461–73.

GREENWOOD, M., and WOODS, H. M. (1919) *The Incidence of Industrial Accidents*. Rep. Industr. Hlth. Res. Board. (Pink Reports). No. 4. Her Majesty's Stationery Office, London.

GUNZBURG, H. C. (1948) "Experiments in the improvement of reading in a group of educationally subnormal boys." *J. ment. Sci.* **94**, 103.

HARRISON, R. (1941) "Personal tempo and the interrelationship of voluntary and maximal rates of movement." *J. Gen. Psychol.* **24**, 343–79.

HEALY, W., and BRONNER, A. (1936) *New Light on Delinquency and its Treatment*. Yale Univ. Press, New Haven.

HEATH, S. R. (Jun.) (1942) "Rail walking performance as related to mental age and aetiological type among the mentally retarded." *Amer. J. Psychol.* **45**, 240–7.

HEGGE, T. G. (1944) "The occupational status of higher grade mental defectives in the present emergency." *Amer. J. ment. Def.* **49**, 86–98.

HENDERSON, D. K., and GILLESPIE, R. D. (1950) *A Text-book of Psychiatry*. Oxford University Press.

HERON, A., and VENABLES, P. H. (1956) *Personal communication*.

HERTZMAN, M., ORLANSKY, J., and SEITZ, C. P. (1944) "Personality organisation and anoxia tolerance." *Psychosom. Med.* **6**, 317–31.

HEUYER, G., PIERON, H., PIERON, H. (Mme.) and SAUVY, A. (1950) *Le Niveau Intellectuel des Enfants d'Age Scolaire*. Paris.

HILLIARD, L. T., and MUNDY, LYDIA (1954) "Diagnostic Problems in the feeble-minded." *Lancet*. **2**, 644–6.

HIMMELWEIT, H. T. (1945) "A study of temperament of neurotic persons by means of level of aspiration tests." Ph.D. Thesis. Univ. of London.

HOLT, I. (1943) "Mental defectives in industry." *Amer. J. ment. Def.* **48**, 124–5.

HONZIK, M. P., MacFARLANE, J. W., and ALLEN, C. (1948) "The stability of mental test performance between two and eighteen years." *J. Exp. Educ.* **17**, 309–24.

HUNT, J. McV., and COFER, C. (1944) Psychological Deficit, in *Personality and the Behaviour Disorders* (J. McV. HUNT, ed.). Vol. II, 971–1032. Ronald Press, New York.

JOLLES, I. (1947) "A study of mental deficiency by the Rorschach technique." *Amer. J. ment. Def.* **52**, 37–42.

JONES, MAXWELL (1944) "Psychological responses to stress in neurotic patients." *Psychosom. Med.* **6**, 308–10.

JONES, MAXWELL (1948) "Psychological response to stress in neurotic patients." *J. ment. Sci.* **94**, 392–427.

JONES, MAXWELL (1955) *Minutes of Evidence of the Royal Commission on the Law Relating to Mental Illness and Mental Deficiency*, 30th day. Her Majesty's Stationery Office, London.

KAILA, M. (1942) Über die Durchschnittshäufigkeit der Geisteskrankheiten und des Schwachsinns in Finland. *Acta. psychiat. et neurol.* **17**, 47.

KALLMAN, F. J., *et al.* (1941) "The role of mental deficiency in the incidence of schizophrenia." *Amer. J. ment. Def.* **45**, 514–39.

KANNER, L. (1947) *Child Psychiatry.* Charles C. Thomas, Springfield, Ill.

KANNER, L. (1943–44) "The role of the school in the treatment of the rejected child." *The Nervous Child.* **3**, 236–48.

KANNER, L. (1948) *A Miniature Text-book of Mental Deficiency.* Child Care Publicns., New York.

KAPLAN, O. (1939) Life expectancy of low grade mental defectives. *Psychol. Bull.* **36**, 513.

KAPLAN, O. (1940) "Life expectancy of low-grade mental defectives." *Psychol. Rev.* **3**, 295–306.

KARPMAN, B. (1948) "The myth of the psychopathic personality." *Amer. J. Psychiat.*, 523–34.

KENNEDY, R. J. R. (1948) *The Social Adjustment of Morons in Connecticut City.* Mansfield Southbury Social Service, Hartford Conn.

KINDER, E. F., CHASE, A., and BUCK, E. W. (1941) "Data secured during a follow up study of girls discharged from supervised parole from Letchworth village." *Amer. J. ment. Def.* **45**, 572–8.

KINGSLEY, L. V., and HYDE, R. W. (1945) "The health and occupational adequacy of the mentally deficient." *J. abnorm. soc. Psychol.* **40**, 37–46.

KLINEBERG, O. (1940) *Social Psychology.* Henry Holt, New York.

KREMER, A. (1942) "The nature of persistence." *Studies in Psychology and Psychiatry. Cathol. Univer. of America.* Vol. V.

LAING, J. K. C. (1952) "The education and training of mental defectives at Darenth Park." *Mental Health* (London). **12**, 3–10.

LEMKAU, P., TIETZE, C., and COOPER, M. (1942) Mental hygiene problems in an urban district; third paper. *Ment. Hyg.*, N.Y. **26**, 275–88.

LEWIN, K. (1942) Time perspective and morale, in *Civilian Morale* (GOODWIN WATSON, ed.).

LIPPITT, R. (1940) "An analysis of group reactions to three types of experimentally created social climates." Unpublished Doctoral Thesis, State Univer. of Iowa.

LIPPITT, R., and WHITE, R. K. (1947) "An experimental study of leadership and group life," in *Readings in Social Psychology* (T. L. NEWCOMB, E. L. HARTLEY *et al.*, eds.). Henry Holt, New York.

LOOS, F. M., and TIZARD, J. (1955) "The employment of adult imbeciles in a hospital workshop." *Amer. J. ment. Def.* **59**, 395–403.

LOUTTIT, C. M. (1947) *Clinical Psychology.* Harper, New York.

LOWREY, L. G. (1944) "Delinquent and criminal personalities," in *Personality and the behaviour disorders* (J. McV. HUNT, ed.). II, 794–821. Ronald Press, New York.

LUBIN, A. (1951) "Some contributions to the testing of psychological hypotheses by means of statistical multi-variate analysis." Ph.D. Thesis. University of London Library.

LUBIN, A., and SUMMERFIELD, A. (1951) "A square root method of selecting a minimum set of variables in multiple regression." *Psychometrika.* **16,** 425–37.

LURIA, A. R. (1932) *The Nature of Human Conflict or Emotion Conflict, and Will.* Moscow. Liveright Inc., New York (trans. W. H. GANTT).

MACKWORTH, N. H. (1950) *Researches on the Measurement of Human Performance.* Her Majesty's Stationery Office, London.

MACMAHON, J. F. (1955) *Minutes of Evidence of the Royal Commission on the Law Relating to Mental Illness and Mental Deficiency,* 30*th day.* Her Majesty's Stationery Office, London.

MARKOWE, M., and BARBER, L. E. D. (1953) Mental health in relation to the labour turnover of unskilled workers in a large industrial establishment. *Brit. J. prev. Med.* **7,** 205–10.

MARRIOTT, R. (1949) "Size of working group and output." *Occup. Psychol.* **23,** 45–57.

McCULLOCH, T. L. (1947) "Reformulation of the problem of mental deficiency." *Amer. J. ment. Def.* **52,** 130–6.

McFARLAND, R. A., and HUDDLESON, J. H. (1936) "Neurocirculatory reactions in psychoneurosis studied by the Schneider method." *Amer. J. Psychiat.* **93,** 567.

McKEON, R. M. (1946) "Mentally retarded boys in war time." *Ment. Hyg. New York.* **30,** 47–55.

McNEMAR, Q. (1942) *The Revision of the Stanford-Binet Scale.* Houghton Mifflin, Boston.

MENNINGER, W. C. (1948) Facts and statistics of significance for psychiatry. *Bull. Menninger Clin.*

MINSKI, L. (1955) *Minutes of Evidence of South West Metropolitan Regional Hospital Board,* para. 4816. *Royal Commission on the Law Relating to Mental Illness and Mental Deficiency.* Her Majesty's Stationery Office, London.

MUENCH, G. A. (1944) "A follow up of mental defectives after 18 years." *J. abnorm. soc. Psychol.* **39,** 407–18.

National Union of Teachers. (1955) *Minutes of Evidence of the Royal Commission on the Law Relating to Mental Illness and Mental Deficiency,* 28*th day.* Her Majesty's Stationery Office, London.

NEMZIK, C. L. (1933) "The constancy of the I.Q." *Psychol. Bull.* **30,** 143–68.

NEUER, H. (1947) "The relationship between behaviour disorders in children and the syndrome of mental deficiency." *Amer. J. ment. Def.* **52,** 143–7.

O'CONNOR, N. (1951) "Neuroticism and emotional instability in high grade male defectives. *J. Neurol., Neurosurg. and Psychiat.* **14,** 226.

O'CONNOR, N. (1951) "Personality variables which affect the vocational and social efficiency of high grade defectives." Ph.D. Thesis. University of London Library.

O'CONNOR, N. (1952) "The prediction of psychological stability and anxiety-aggressiveness etc." *J. gen. Psychol.* **46**, 3–17.

O'CONNOR, N., and LOOS, F. L. (to appear) "The work record of backward boys."

O'CONNOR, N., and CLARIDGE, G. (1955) "The effect of goal-setting and encouragement on the performance of imbecile men." *Quart. J. Exptal. Psychol.* **7**, 37–45.

O'CONNOR, N., and TIZARD, J. (1951) "Predicting the occupational adequacy of certified mental defectives." *Occup. Psychol.* **25**, 205–11.

O'CONNOR, N., and TIZARD, J. (1954) "A survey of patients in twelve mental deficiency institutions." *Brit. Med. J.* **1**, 16–18.

O'CONNOR, N., and YONGE, K. A. (1955) "Methods of evaluating the group psychotherapy of unstable defective delinquents." *J. genet. Psychol.* (in press).

PATTERSON, R. M. (1950) "Psychiatric treatment of institutionalised delinquent adolescent girls." *Dis. nerv. Syst.* **11**, 227–32.

PENROSE, L. S. (1938) *A Clinical and Genetic Study of 1280 Cases of Mental Defect.* M.R.C. Special Report. No. 229. Her Majesty's Stationery Office, London.

PENROSE, L. S. (1949) *The Biology of Mental Defect.* Sidgwick & Jackson, London.

PENROSE, L. S. (1949) "The incidence of mongolism in the general population." *J. ment. Sci.* **95**, 685.

PENROSE, L. S. (1950) "Genetic influences on the intelligence level of the population." *Brit. J. Psychol.* **40**, 128–36.

PINEL, P. (1806) *Treatise on Insanity* (trans. D. D. DAVIS). Cadell and Davies, London.

POLLOCK, H. M. (1944) Mental disease among mental defectives. *Amer. J. Psychiat.* **101**, 361.

PORTEUS, S. D. (1941) *The Practice of Clinical Psychology.* American Book Co., New York.

RANK, B. (1949) "Adaptation of psychoanalytic techniques for treatment of children with atypical development." *Amer. J. Orthopsychiat.* **19**, 130–9.

ROETHLISBERGER, F. J., and DICKINSON, W. J. (1949) *Management and the Worker.* Harvard University Press, Cambridge, U.S.A.

ROSENZWEIG, S. (1938) "Frustration as an experimental problem." *Character and Personality.* **7**, 126–8.

RYANS, D. G. (1938) "The meaning of persistence." *J. genet. Psychol.* **19**, 79–96.

SARASON, S. B. (1949) *Psychological Problems in Mental Deficiency.* Harper, New York.

SCHNEIDER, E. C., and KARPOVICH, P. V. (1948) *Physiology of Muscular Activity.* Saunders, Philadelphia.

SCOTTISH COUNCIL FOR RESEARCH IN EDUCATION (1923) *The Intelligence of Scottish Children*. University of London Press.

SCOTTISH COUNCIL FOR RESEARCH IN EDUCATION (1949) *The Trend of Scottish Intelligence*. University of London Press.

SCOTTISH COUNCIL FOR RESEARCH IN EDUCATION (1953) *Social Implications of the 1947 Scottish Mental Survey*. University of London Press.

SEARS, P. S. (1940) "Level of aspiration in academically successful and academically unsuccessful children." *J. abnorm. soc. Psychol.* **35,** 498–536.

SEGUIN, E. (1846) *Traitement Morale, Hygeine et Education des Idiots.* J. B. Bailliere, Paris and London.

SHERIF, M. (1948) *An Outline of Social Psychology*. Harper, New York.

SJÖGREN, T. (1948) "Genetic-statistical and psychiatric investigations of a West Swedish population." *Acta. psychiat. et neurol.* Suppl. 52. Copenhagen.

SKEELS, H. M., and HARMS, E. (1948) Children with inferior social histories. *J. genet. Psychol.* **72,** 283–94.

SLAVSON, S. R. (1947) *The Practice of Group Therapy*. Pushkin, London.

SLOAN, W. (1947) "Mental deficiency as a symptom of personality disturbance." *Amer. J. ment. Def.* **52,** 31–6.

SMITH, MAY., and ZAKI, A. (1948) "The nervous temperament." *Egyp. J. Psychol.* **4,**

STODDARD, G. D. (1943) *The Meaning of Intelligence*. Macmillan, New York.

STRÖMGREN, E. (1938) *Beiträge zur psychiatrischen Erblehre*. Ejnar Munsksgaard, Copenhagen.

TERMAN, L. M., and MERRILL, M. A. (1937) *Measuring Intelligence*. London, Harrap.

THOMAS, B. E. (1943) "A study of factors used to make a prognosis of social adjustment." *Amer. J. ment. Def.* **47,** 334–6.

THOMPSON, L. A. (Jun.) (1928–30) "Measuring susceptibility to monotony." *Personnel J.* **8,** 172.

THORNDIKE, R. L. (1940) "Constancy of the I.Q." *Psychol. Bull.*, **37,** 167–86.

THORNDIKE, R. L. (1949) *Personnel selection; test and measurement techniques*. John Wiley & Sons, New York.

THORNTON, G. R. (1939) "A factor analysis of tests designed to measure persistence." *Psychol. Monogr.* **51,** No. 229.

TIETZE, C. (1943) "Notes on the incidence of mental disease in the State of New York." *Amer. J. Psychiat.* 100.

TIZARD, J. (1950) "The abilities of adolescent and adult high-grade male defectives." *J. ment. Sci.* **96,** 889–907.

TIZARD, J. (1951a) "The Porteus maze test and intelligence. A critical survey." *Brit. J. educ. Psychol.* **21,** 172–85.

TIZARD, J. (1951b) "An experimental study of the vocational adjustment of subnormal boys." Ph.D. Thesis. University of London.

TIZARD, J. (1953a) "The effects of different types of supervision on the behaviour of mental defectives in a sheltered workshop." *Amer. J. ment. Def.* **58**, 143–61.

TIZARD, J. (1953b) "The prevalence of mental subnormality." *Bull. World Hlth. Org.* **9**, 423–40.

TIARZD, J. (1955) "The future of mental deficiency legislation in England." *Medico-legal Journal*, July.

TIZARD, J., and O'CONNOR, N. (1950) "The employability of high-grade mental defectives." I and II. *Amer. J. ment. Def.* **54**, 563–76; **55**, 144–57.

TIZARD, J., and O'CONNOR, N. (1952) "The occupational adaptation of high-grade mental defectives." *Lancet.* **2**, 620.

TREDGOLD, A. F. (1947) *A Textbook of Mental Deficiency.* Bailliere Tindall and Cox, London.

TREDGOLD, A. F., and TREDGOLD, R. F. (1951) *A Textbook of Mental Deficiency.* Bailliere Tindall and Cox, London.

TULCHIN, S. H. (1939) *Intelligence and Crime.* University of Chicago Press.

VERNON, H. M. (1921) *Industrial Fatigue and Efficiency.* Routledge, London.

VERNON, P. E. (1937) "A study of the norms and validity of certain mental tests at a child guidance clinic." *Brit. J. educ. Psychol.* **7**, 72–88; 115–37.

WALLIN, J. E. W. (1949) *Children with mental and physical handicaps.* Staples Press, London.

WALTON, D., and BEGG, T. L. (1955) "Adult imbeciles." *Lancet.* II, 616–17.

WEAVER, T. R. (1946) "The incidence of maladjustment among mental defectives in a military environment." *Amer. J. ment. Def.* **51**, 238–46.

WECHSLER, D. (1944) *The Measurement of Adult Intelligence.* Williams & Wilkins, Baltimore.

WEINER, M. (1955) "An investigation into psychological factors affecting the employability of defectives under statutory supervision." Ph.D. Thesis. University of London.

WENDER, L, (1936) "The dynamics of group psychotherapy, and its application." *J. nerv. ment. Dis.* **84**, 54.

WHITNEY, E. A. (1948) "A statistical study of children admitted to and discharged from Elwyn." *Amer. J. ment. Def.* **53**, 183–6.

WOODROW, H. (1939) "Factors in improvement with practice." *J. Psychol.* **7**, 55–70.

WOODWARD, M. (1955) "The role of low intelligence in delinquency." *Brit. J. Delinqu.* Vol. V, 4, 281–303.

WYATT, S., FROST, L., and STOCK, F. G. L. (1934) *Incentives in Repetitive Work.* Rep. Industr. Hlth. Res. Board (Pink Reports). No. 69. Her Majesty's Stationery Office, London.

WYATT, S., and LANGDON, J. N. (1937) *Fatigue and Boredom in Repetitive Work.* Rep. Industr. Hlth. Res. Board (Pink Reports). No. 77. Her Majesty's Stationery Office, London.

YERKES, R. M. (1921) "Psychological examining in the U.S. army." *Mem. Nat. Acad. Sci.* **15,** Washington Govt. Printing Office.

YONGE, K. A., and O'CONNOR, N. (1954) "Measurable effects of group psychotherapy with defective delinquents." *J. ment. Sci.* **100,** 944–52.

REPORTS

Board of Control (1931) *Colonies for Mental Defectives:* Report of the Departmental Committee appointed by the Board of Control. Her Majesty's Stationery Office, London.

Board of Control (1946) *List of State Institutions, Certified Institutions, Certified Houses and Approved Homes for Mental Defectives in England and Wales.* Her Majesty's Stationery Office, London.

Board of Education and Board of Control (1929) *Report of the Mental Deficiency Committee* (Wood Report). Her Majesty's Stationery Office, London.

Ministry of Education (1945) *Pupils in Need of Special Educational Treatment* (Pamphlet No. 5). Her Majesty's Stationery Office, London.

World Health Organisation (1954) Joint Expert Committee on the Mentally Subnormal Child. *World Hlth. Org. techn. Rep. Ser.* **75.**

World Health Organisation (1948) *Manual of the International Statistical Classification of Diseases, Injuries and Causes of Death.* W.H.O., Geneva.

World Health Organisation (1952) Joint Expert Committee on the Physically Handicapped Child. *World Hlth. Org. techn. Rep. Ser.* 58, 8.

INDEX